Gardner L. Brown

DEDICATION

I should like to dedicate this book to Miss Griffiths, my seventh grade English teacher. She would be flabbergasted.

RESINS IN RUBBER

or

*"What every young compounder should know
about the use of Hydrocarbon Resins in rubber."*

GARDNER L. BROWN

Published by
PENNSYLVANIA INDUSTRIAL CHEMICAL CORP.
Clairton, Pennsylvania 15025

TABLE OF CONTENTS

Chapter V

INTRODUCTION

The actions of a rubber compounder are limited by the boundaries set by the processing requirements of the uncured compounds, the quality standards of the vulcanizate and by economics. New elastomers and new production techniques continually strain to overcome these limitations in the name of "progress." Compounders well know such changes are all too frequently accompanied by difficult processing problems, i.e., tubing, calendering, mixing or building tack.

A compounder often turns to synthetic or natural resins to alleviate some of the side effects of progress. However, as you look for a resin to solve your problem, you may easily become confused by the multiplicity of the resins on the market. Which of the many resins shall you first try?

This is the issue with which this treatise is concerned. Resins are not so much proprietary, secret nostrums as they are complex substances which defy meaningful generic classification. For this reason, as well as for "enlightened self-interest," this text identifies various resins made by the Pennsylvania Industrial Chemical Corporation by their Registered Trademarks* and also gives a generalized description of them by type. Since the Pennsylvania Industrial Chemical Corporation makes the widest variety of hydrocarbon resins, this will give the compounder a working knowledge of the entire field of rubber grade hydrocarbon resins.

Resins are the only commonly used organic compounding ingredients having a high glass transition temperature. Because of this, resins decrease in viscosity at a faster rate than elastomers and oils at common processing and curing temperatures. Improvements in processing and mold flow can therefore be obtained without major effects on the modulus and hardness of the vulcanizate since resins harden again when cooled. Resins, having bulky, inflexible structures, reduce nerve and increase green strength, both of which contribute to good building tack.

---

* PICCO, PICCOLYTE, PICCOCIZER, PICCOLASTIC, PICCOPALE, PICCOTEX, PICCOFLEX, PICCODIENE are Registered Trademarks of the Pennsylvania Industrial Chemical Corporation used on its brands of synthetic resins.

Aromatic resins increase the tensile strength, elongation and resistance to flex cracking of SBR and neoprene vulcanizates using non-black fillers. Whereas coal-derived coumarone indene resins have normally been used for this "organic reinforcement" effect, lower cost petroleum polyindene resins are now the most widely used.

Aliphatic resins are used principally as tackifiers in body stocks, adhesives and in pressure sensitive tapes. Resins with an intermediate amount of aromatic content are used in both applications, i.e., as reinforcing resins and as tackifiers.

The aromatic content, or lack of it, affects the compatibility of a rubber-resin blend. A limited amount of incompatibility is felt to be important in the development of building tack and uncured green strength.

By and large, the use of resins above the level of 15 phr in rubber compounds has not been adequately investigated. By intuition, nearly everyone "knows" this approach won't work. A few, who "don't know it won't work," are finding ways to make it work with accompanying processing and economic advantages.

Never before has such a wide range of low cost, high quality, rubber processing resins been available. Although the choice of the proper resin is still an art, newly developed scientific criteria show promise as we seek to understand what we are already doing.

CHAPTER ONE

WHAT IS AVAILABLE

History of Hydrocarbon Resins

During the coking of coal or the manufacture of coal (city) gas, olefins are produced as a result of the high temperature cracking of organic substances. The aromatic, liquid unsaturates are found in distillation fractions known as light oils or drip oils. For many years, some of these olefins have been polymerized to form resins known as coumarone indene or coal tar resins. They are not, as the name suggests, simple copolymers but contain substantial amounts of styrene and the homologues of styrene and indene. The coumarone content is very low and the name is not really descriptive of their composition. The situation has been complicated further by the development of aromatic petroleum resins which contain essentially the same monomers. In view of the low coumarone content, attempts have been made to describe all of these resins more accurately as "polyindene" resins. This term has never really caught on since the expression "coumarone indene" has come to refer to a compounding effect rather than to the chemical composition of a substance. Today, all of them are commonly referred to as coumarone indene resins.

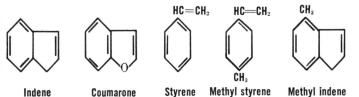

| Indene | Coumarone | Styrene | Methyl styrene | Methyl indene |

Until 1945 coal tar resins were the only synthetic hydrocarbon resins used in rubber compounding. Although the individual uses were generally quite small, the number of applications was large. Of the 216 formulations listed in the 1958 Vanderbilt Handbook, 66 of them (30%) call for some form of hydrocarbon resin. Over the years, many processing problems have been solved by the simple inclusion of small amounts of coumarone indene resin. It is common today to add five parts of resin to a newly developed laboratory compound the second time it is processed on factory equipment, assuming the usual processing problems developed the first time through.

Reinforcing Effect

World War II forced the use of new elastomers and introduced new quality and processing problems. One of the problems faced by the early compounders of SBR was that the use of the traditional non-reinforcing fillers such as whiting, blanc fixe, etc., produced vulcanizates with very poor tensile strength values, on the order of 500 to 700 psi. It was soon discovered that coumarone indene resins had a synergistic effect on such compounds, improving tensiles to the point that commercial articles could be made from them.

TABLE 1.
(Reference 1)
The Effect of Coumarone Indene Resin On An
SBR Vulcanizate Containing 50 Volumes of Lithopone
Cure 15 minutes at 316°F.

Coumarone Indene Resin Content phr	Modulus, psi at 300%	500%	Tensile psi	Elongation %	Shore A Hardness
0	275	—	475	400	58
5	225	—	475	455	57
10	150	450	625	540	55
20	150	275	1525	715	49
40	75	150	1775	870	39

This phenomenon was dubbed the "organic reinforcement" effect by Blake[2] who reported the use of a coumarone indene resin in combination with a non-reinforcing filler brings about an increase in the tensile product (TxE) of from two to seven times as shown in Figure 1. When used without combination, the improvement in physical properties is comparatively insignificant. This allowed the wire and cable industry to produce satisfactory non-carbon black insulations from SBR. Because of its reasonable cost and substantial reinforcing effect, coumarone indene resins have been universally used in SBR insulating compounds containing mineral fillers.

SBR soling once failed prematurely due to flex cracking. It was discovered the addition of 10 to 15 parts of a coumarone indene resin would correct this deficiency without much effect on other properties of the soling. In present day, leather-hard soling compounds, the tensile improvement noticed in softer compounds is not achieved. However, Table 2 illustrates the

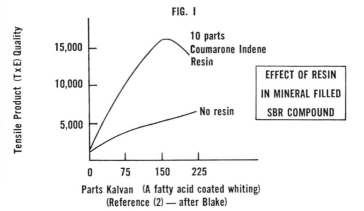

FIG. I

EFFECT OF RESIN
IN MINERAL FILLED
SBR COMPOUND

Parts Kalvan   (A fatty acid coated whiting)
(Reference (2) — after Blake)

improvement in flex resistance and processing resulting from the incorporation of 15 parts of coumarone indene resin in an SBR slab soling compound.[3] The effect is rather dramatic, as one would not always expect to improve flex by the addition of a brittle substance.

TABLE 2
(Reference 3)
EFFECT OF RESIN ON PROCESSING & FLEX — SBR SLAB SOLE

	Control No Resin	10 phr Coumarone Indene Resin
Scorch (MS 280°F)		
Time to 10 point rise	14′ 0″	19″ 30″
4′ Reading (Mooney units)	72	45.5
Ross Cut Growth		
Cycles to 0.5 in. growth	15,000	60,000

This effect is generally true for all elastomers having poor cured gum strength. Early authors [1, 4] suggest the improvement might be due to the solubilizing effect of the resin on the sulfur, resulting in an improved dispersion of the sulfur. Today, it is more common to speak of resins as having a wetting action on the fillers, resulting in their improved dispersion. A more probable answer, at least in regards to flex, is the effect of resins on the creep and relaxation properties of the vulcanizate. The viscous characteristics of a compound dissipate the stresses at the tip of a growing crack and, hence, retard its growth. Resins contribute more to the viscous nature of a stock than to its elastic component.

Although the reasons are still obscure, the organic reinforce-

5

The first commercial butadiene in the U.S. was made in this unit. It was also the source of raw materials for the first petroleum resins in the world. Location: Chester, Pennsylvania.

ment effect is quite real. The use of resins in hose compounds, matting, wire insulation and soling has developed into a major marketing area for coumarone indene resins and, later, their petroleum derived counterparts.

The optimum properties are generally found with the use of 10 to 15 parts of resin. However, it is becoming more common to use resin at the 25 phr level, using the resin as an extender as well as for its enhancement of physicals. Modern technology has reduced the price of these resins by $1/3$, causing compounders to re-examine the economics of their existing formulations. The old adage that "if a little bit is good, why not add a lot?" is not always wrong.

In black loaded stocks, resins are generally used because of a processing requirement instead of a vulcanizate quality consideration. With the modern day piece work form of payment, the mandate not to rock the factory routine (to make the stock "run right") is strong indeed. Until replaced by more effective resins, coumarone indene resins were used at the 5 part level for many years as a tackifier for passenger tire carcass stocks. Resins are also used in black loaded stocks to improve tear resistance and to reduce tread groove cracking. This latter observation accounts for the large volumes of resin used in camelback.

These and other new developments brought about a shortage of resins during World War II since only limited amounts of the coal derived unsaturates were available.

Petroleum Resins

During and prior to World War II, the United Gas Improvement Company had been conducting large scale experiments in Chester, Pennsylvania. Their objective was to crack oil, not for gasoline, but for gas to extend their supplies of water gas for domestic distribution in the Philadelphia area.[5] This was before natural gas was available all over the country. Picco observed the parallels between the cracking of oil and the coking of coal and discovered the unsaturates from the United Gas (known as UGITE) process could be polymerized to form resins very much like the coal tar resins.

In 1945 Picco bought the UGITE Chester plant and the patent estates relating to this process. At the same time, various large oil companies were getting into the petrochemical business more heavily, cracking oil to produce gas to be used in the chemical industry, i.e., butadiene, ethylene, etc. From the UGITE experience, Picco was able to guide such companies to produce unsaturates suitable for resin manufacture, as well as the gas and solvents needed by the oil companies. This was the beginning of the ever widening variety of petroleum resins which directly reflects the growing complexity of petrochemical cracking operations. Today the term "Petroleum Resin" has virtually no meaning, compared to the expression "coal tar resins," and this is due to the widely different resins stemming from this source.

Picco 100-5 resin was the first commercially produced product from this new development in petroleum engineering. The "100" refers to the ball and ring softening point of the resin in °C; the "5" represents the maximum color of the resin on the coal tar scale. With a few exceptions, this is the basis for identifying the varying grades of Picco resins.

The Picco 100-5 resin proved to be a good match for the coal tar derivatives such as Picco N-100-1½ resin in all respects except for the final color in a cured compound. Lighter colored versions of Picco 100-5 resin (Picco 100-3) are available today and, together with a new product (Picco 6100-1½ resin), are considered to be equal to, or better than, the coal tar resins in cured color. Today's resins are definitely better than the older ones in resistance to discoloration by ultraviolet light, simply because the raw materials are now available in a much more refined state.

Since 1945, the use of coal tar resins has steadily declined and today represent only a very small percentage of the resins used by the rubber industry. This is effective testimony to the quality of today's aromatic petroleum resins.

Today's terminology should abandon the use of the phrases, "coumarone-indene" resins, coal tar resins and petroleum resins. In their place, the expressions, aromatic hydrocarbon resins, semi-aromatic hydrocarbon resins, and non-aromatic hydrocarbon (or aliphatic) resins should be used. Reasons for this are bound up in the greater sophistication of chemical processes which has evolved since World War II. Benzene and toluene, for instance, are no longer solely derived from coal tar; thus, it is not entirely correct to call them "coal tar" chemicals. By the same token, resin raw materials containing the indenes characteristic of coumarone indene resins also come from the petrochemical industry, and their source is irrelevant.

Polyterpene Resins

The use of resins by the rubber industry has expanded, not only because of polymer changes but because a wider variety of resins is now available. While most of these are from petroleum derived unsaturates, at least one major resin used in rubber is based on raw materials derived from the fractionation of turpentine.

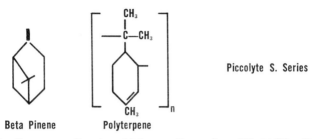

Beta Pinene   Polyterpene

Piccolyte S. Series

The PICCOLYTE S resin, which actually predates World War II, is made from beta pinene. It is an aliphatic resin in contrast to the very aromatic hydrocarbon resins just discussed. PICCOLYTE resin functions very effectively as a tackifier without the habit of drying out in a short period of time. It is used at high concentrations (50/50) with natural rubber or polyisobutylene to formulate pressure sensitive adhesives. Today, the world supply of beta pinene barely meets the requirements of the adhesive industry and a similar resin has been developed. The PICCOLYTE ALPHA resins are made from alpha pinene, another, more abundant constituent of turpentine. While somewhat different in performance compared to the beta polymers, the ALPHA resins can be formulated with rubbers to perform in this market and is expected to resolve the beta pinene supply problem which now exists. The PICCOLYTE ALPHA resin, unlike the beta polymers, can be used to produce SBR based pressure sensitive adhesives, indicating a greater versatility for the new resin.

Aliphatic Resins

In 1952 PICCOPALE resin was developed. Like PICCOLYTE resin, it is aliphatic but is derived instead from petroleum sources. This simple fact gives PICCOPALE resin the virtue of lower cost and nearly unlimited availability. PICCOPALE 100-SF resin finds its greatest use as a tackifier and, in fact, is today the world's most widely used resin tackifier for tire carcass stocks. PICCOPALE resin is moderately priced and has an advantage in carcass stocks in that large amounts, compared to liquids, can be used without introducing insurmountable side effects, i.e., cure rate, modulus, etc. It is being used at increasingly higher levels to allow the reduction of the natural rubber content of skim stocks and cushion gum compounds. Not only is this an economy measure but, since natural rubber vulcanizates revert on overcure, this compounding technique allows the use of higher temperature curing.

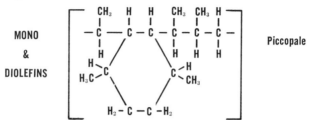

MONO & DIOLEFINS — Piccopale

Skim stocks tackified with PICCOPALE 100-SF resin are recognized as having excellent tack retention properties, allowing for complex factory operations where the oldest rolls of stock are not always used first. Compounders have commented too, that PICCOPALE resin containing stocks are less susceptible to the tack variations which are usually blamed on the weather. Naturally, comments based on tire experience carry over to the hose and belting field.

New tire technology has disrupted the conventional techniques of extending carcass stocks with reclaim or oil extended polymers. Each method of extension is, of course, limited by quality or processing considerations. PICCOPALE resin has different limiting parameters allowing its use as an extender where older methods cannot be employed. For instance, highly extended stocks tend to be mushy and doughy but the use of resins gives stocks having more green strength and higher dynamic modulus. Although in use at the 15 to 25 part level, the absolute limits of resin extension have not yet been determined.

Cyclopentadiene Resins

There is always a market for a very low cost, non-staining resin. Developments in the petrochemical industry over the past few years have introduced cyclopentadiene or "reactive" resins. (PICCODIENE Resin Series)

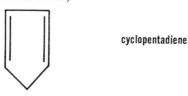

cyclopentadiene

PICCOPALE RESIN UNIT — Baton Rouge, Louisiana.

One of the most modern rubber resin producing plants, this PICCOPALE resin unit is part of the giant Mississippi River petrochemical complex at Baton Rouge.

PICCOPALE resin is one of the most important of all hydrocarbon resins used in rubber compounding.

PICCODIENE 14215-SRG resin is made from low cost, refinery by-product streams which contain substantial amounts of dicyclopentadiene. While this portion of the unsaturates would polymerize to give a cyclo-aliphatic structure, the balance of the unsaturates are quite aromatic, not unlike the polyindene resins. The over-all effect is to produce a resin of intermediate aromatic content. This gives the PICCODIENE resins a remarkable versatility in that they perform well both as tackifiers and in the organic reinforcement effect. While non-staining, they are inferior to our other grades of light colored resins in terms of cured color.

The cyclopentadiene resins contain unsaturation which will react with paint oils containing conjugated double bonds under the high temperatures of varnish cooking. Hence, the reference to "reactive" resins. While slightly cure retarding, the PICCODIENE resins are essentially non-reactive as far as rubber compounding is concerned.

Resinex Resins

The product known as RESINEX* was developed in 1945, the same time as the PICCO 100-5 resin and as a result of the UGITE cracking process. It is a dark resin but with a very low content of carbonaceous material. Therefore, despite its dark color, it does not have very much tinting strength and can be used in colored stocks such as brown and dark red.

The composition of the product RESINEX is complex and can best be described as a polynuclear aromatic. While not precisely a coumarone indene resin, it functions like one in regard to the organic reinforcement effect. It is used in large volumes by the soling industry, particularly in neoprene stocks. It is also widely used in camelback compounds. At low levels it functions to reduce groove cracking and also as a processing aid. At the 15 part level, compounders report it gives good building tack, maintains modulus well, incorporates easily, and results in only a very slight loss in treadwear. When used at the 25 part level it serves as an extender in the lower cost grades of camelback. It is the lowest cost Picco resin; it stains.

Miscellaneous Resins

The resins yet to be described fall into one of two categories. Either they are modifications of a major resin type or are completely unrelated to the coal-petroleum story underlying the developments to this date.

*RESINEX is the registered trademark of the Harwick Standard Chemical Co. for its brand of dark, aromatic, hydrocarbon resins.

Picco N-25-5 resin is a low molecular weight aromatic hydro-carbon with a ball and ring softening point of 25°C. It is used in neoprene and nitrile stocks as a processing aid. It is also used extensively in very low Mooney compounds because it mixes easily compared to its higher softening point relatives. Picco Aromatic Plasticizer 25-5 resin is a soft, semi-aromatic product used mostly as a tackifier in SBR latex adhesives. Until recently it was not widely used in neoprene and nitrile because of slow mixing speeds. In dry liquid concentrate form however, it handles very well and the use of this lower cost material is growing rapidly.

The products, Piccocizer 30, Dipolymer Oil and Resinex L4, are all aromatic liquids used to tackify neoprene friction stocks and as plasticizers for nitrile compounds. Most rubber hydrocarbon resins are used in the state of polymerization in-volving the joining of 5 to 7 monomer units. The aromatic liquids represent mostly only 2 monomer units.

The Picco 480 resins are styrenated coumarone indene resins. The styrene content provides an extra improvement in shore hardness while acting as a reinforcing resin in shoe soling.

With newer processing techniques available, new grades of Piccopale resin, notably Piccopale 200 Series, will open new applications for resins in rubber processing.

The other products, Piccotex, Piccoflex and Piccolastic resins, are made from pure monomers in contrast to the petro-leum and coal tar resins. Piccotex resin is the copolymer of alpha methyl styrene and vinyl toluene. It is a water white, aromatic resin and performs very well in the organic reinforce-ment effect. Its color and color stability are, of course, its out-standing characteristics.

The common rubber processing resin is a very brittle solid with very little mechanical strength. In contrast, the Piccoflex and Piccolastic resins are tough and horny materials. Styrene is a major ingredient in both resins. The toughness of these resins reflects in higher modulus and hardness values compared to the more brittle resins.

The available literature [6] deals with each of these products in more detail and provides considerable technical data. Several resins are also available in emulsion form, for use in the latex field. In general, these systems perform functions which somewhat comparable to those obtained in dry rubber com-pounding. The reader is referred to the supplementary literature [7] for more specific information.

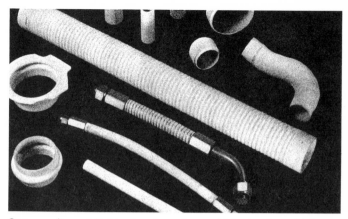

Compounding of light-colored products which also have high performance standards are possible with the use of several grades of light hydrocarbon resins.

CHAPTER TWO

COMPOUNDING RULES
OF THUMB

While the use of resins in rubber is still more of an art than a science, it is not always necessary to repeat experiments others have made countless times. The following can serve you as easily remembered "rules of thumb."

If you are looking for a general improvement in the physicals of mineral loaded stocks (the organic reinforcement effect), try PICCO 6100-1-½ resin for light colored stocks and RESINEX resin for dark stocks where staining is not a problem. These are the "normal" resins for this usage. Easier processing will be an added dividend.

The same resins would be the choice as general purpose processing aids.

If you are looking for a tackifier, try PICCOPALE 100-SF resin in stocks containing at least some natural rubber. For synthetic elastomers, try the resins: PICCOLYTE ALPHA 115, PICCO 6100-1½, RESINEX 100 or PICCO N-25-5.

If lower costs are your goal, for a system already functioning well, try the PICCODIENE series, 14215-SRG for tackifying and 2215-SRG, a lighter colored variety, for tan stocks. If you are already using 5 parts of resin, try 10 parts, since resins are generally less expensive than overall compound raw material costs.

Perhaps one day we can predict the detailed performance of a resin-rubber composite by an understanding of solubility parameters, glass transition temperatures and the like. Although we now do this to a degree, until that day comes, the best we can do is to try the resins "most likely to succeed" and then evaluate their variations as we search for additional improvements in specific areas of concern.

Manufacture of automotive tires involves from five to seven different specific applications of hydrocarbon resins.

CHAPTER THREE

QUALITIES RESINS HAVE
IN COMMON

GLASS TRANSITION TEMPERATURES

Compared to elastomers, rubber processing resins are characterized by low molecular weight and a high ball and ring softening point. As rubber is cooled it loses flexibility, becomes leathery and, if cooled sufficiently, changes into a hard resinous substance. The temperature at which amorphous, thermoplastic materials become "glassy" is known as the glass transition temperature (Tg). It is a physical property now being widely used, not only to differentiate between resins and elastomers, but also to characterize elastomers themselves. The glass transition temperature is quite different from the melting point of crystalline substances. Being amorphous, resins have softening points but not melting points.

As compounding ingredients, resins are unique since they are the only commonly used thermoplastic additives having a high glass transition temperature. Table 3 illustrates the wide disparity between the Tg of elastomers and oils and that of resins.

TABLE 3
Glass Transition Temperatures of
Elastomers, Oils and Resins
(Reference #8)

MATERIAL	Tg, °C.
Polybutadiene	— 95 to — 106
Natural Rubber	— 68.5
EPR (50 molar % Ethylene)	— 62
SBR 1500	— 52
Neoprene GNA	— 43
Oils	— 40 to — 90
Resins	+50 to +100

The glass transition temperature is a function of the flexibility of the polymer chain and a measure of the amount of room, or free volume, required for the chain (or part of it) to turn about. When a substance is heated, the increased kinetic energy of the molecules causes expansion, thus creating more free volume within which molecular motion can occur. Figure 2 shows the effect on specific volume as a polymer passes through its glass transition temperature.[9] We expect things to shrink and become more dense when they are cooled. The sharp change in the rate of shrinking, associated with Tg, indicates the free volume in the system has been reduced to a critical point whereby further shrinkage is inhibited by the interference of one molecule with another. Similar effects are noted in the measurements of thermal conductivity, refractive index, stiffness, heat content, and dielectric loss.[9]

FIG. 2
Volume Temperature Curves of Thermoplastic Materials

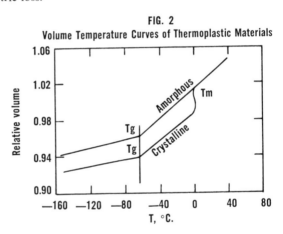

Resin molecules need more "elbow room" than sleek elastomer chains before molecular movement can take place. Resins have fewer points for bond rotation and have bulky side groups. Resins therefore require higher temperatures to achieve appreciable molecular motion. The ability of molecules to move about implies softness and a lower modulus of elasticity in comparison with polymers wherein molecular motion has been restricted by low temperatures. Figure 3 illustrates the phenomenon graphically.

The low molecular weight of rubber processing resins precludes any significant load bearing capability; hence, it is customary to measure the viscosity of resins rather than the modulus. A convenient test is the ball and ring softening point measuring the temperature at which the resin approximates viscosity of one million poises.

18

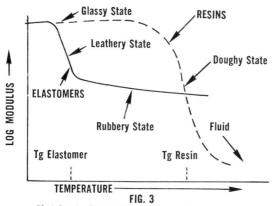

FIG. 3
Modulus vs. Temperature Curves typical of rubber
and to be expected for resins.

Viscosity Change

The common hydrocarbon resin used in rubber has a ball and ring softening point of 100°C. Such a resin is in a glassy state at room temperature and, if we assume it will still be in the glassy state at 50°C, its viscosity at this temperature will be about 10^{13} poises[10]. Like the national debt this is a large number. By heating the resin from 50°C to 100°C, its viscosity will be reduced to about 10^6 poises, a difference of 9,999,999,000,000 poises. By heating to 150°C, the viscosity will be in the order of 100 poises, a difference of 999,900 poises for this second 50°C increment of heat. While this represents a significant viscosity change, it does not begin to compare with the huge change caused by the first heating increment.

The fact that resins change viscosity with heat most rapidly in the glass transition temperature region[10] also means they exert their greatest softening effect at common rubber processing and curing temperatures. While elastomers and oils change viscosity with heat, the rate of change is not as rapid at curing and processing temperatures, compared to resins, since these temperatures are well above the glass transition temperatures of oils and elastomers. This is a most important characteristic held in common by thermoplastic rubber processing resins.

While resins change viscosity rapidly compared with elastomers, the change is very slow in comparison with the manner in which a crystalline material melts, paraffin wax being a good example.

19

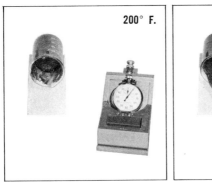

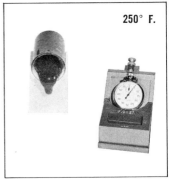

A series of photographs which convey the thermoplastic changes of PICCOPALE 100 SF resin over a range of temperatures. The picture

As the photographs in Figure 4 demonstrate, resins exist in a soft condition over a rather wide range of temperatures. The pictures do not show that the resin is also tacky. Heat acts much like a solvent on resin. As a solvent-resin film dries it becomes tacky in between the fluid and hard stages. For a standard resin with a ball and ring softening point of 212°F, the range over which it remains tacky is about 75°F. Resins are commonly used to make batches "knit" during mixing so they will not dump dry and crumbly. The sticky nature of resins at common mixing temperatures must have a great deal to do with the ability of resins to perform in this manner.

Resin Action in Rubber Stocks

The organic reinforcement effect of resins in mineral filled SBR compounds is frequently explained by a reference to the "improved wetting" of pigments and a beneficial effect on pigment dispersion brought about by the resin. The dispersion of zinc oxide, whiting and sulfur may be improved by coating the particles with a polar substance to alter the electrostatic properties of the material. Although there is no experimental evidence available, it is more likely that non-polar hydrocarbon resins produce a similar effect by virtue of their non-slippery physical condition at mixing temperatures.

Once the stock has returned to room temperature, after processing or curing, resins will exert their normal hardening effect by regaining their glass-like consistency. This simple fact affects cured hardness, modulus and green strength, especially in comparison with oils. The degree of the effect is felt to be a function of the compatibility of the resin with the balance of the

was taken five seconds after the beakers of heated resin were tipped over.

compound and is dealt with at greater length in the section on "How Resins Differ."

For cured stocks, this means we can achieve processing softness or mold flow without much effect on the cured hardness or modulus, an important characteristic in the soling field. Resins are often used without also increasing the filler content, in contrast to the use of liquid softeners. Resins are hydrocarbons and chemically more like rubber than hard fillers.

For uncured stocks, it means we can add larger amounts of resinous tackifiers, compared to liquids, without getting mushy, doughy compounds. Resins, therefore, act to improve green strength without as many undesirable side effects on the dryness of the stock and heat buildup in the vulcanizate as when other modifiers, such as certain types of carbon black, are added for the same purpose. One might well increase green strength by adding more natural rubber but natural rubber is a dirty word to those trying to reduce tire curing cycles or improve the aging properties of passenger tires.

These properties make resins attractive as extenders as well as softeners. Compounders sometimes find they can add 10 to 15 parts of resin on top of a stock already extended to the limit with oils and fillers, yet, remain within specification limits. Others have found they can replace part of the oil with an increased amount of resin. Some compounders prefer to think in terms of replacing part of the expensive elastomer with lower cost resins.

While oils are low cost compounding ingredients, their benefits are limited if the compound will not tolerate much softener. However, if it is possible to replace 5 parts of oil

21

with 10 or 15 parts of resin, the economics begin to look favorable for the resin route, since resins are generally less expensive than the overall compound cost.

Resins have been used for a long time in hose compounds to keep the extruded tube from collapsing. Resins also serve to control die swell by reducing the nerve of the stock. When vacuum formed mats were the rage for automobiles, resins were added to improve the tear resistance of the uncured mat. More recently, resins have found application in tire innerliner compounds, not just for building tack but to reduce the movement of the stock during the early stages of the curing cycle.

Obtaining Tack

Certain resins are widely used as tackifiers, especially for building tack as required in "plied up" products such as tires, belts and some types of hose. Some resins do not function as tackifiers and the difference between those that do and those that do not appears to be a matter of differences in compatibility and stability. This will be discussed further in the section on "How Resins Differ."

However, resins "in general" do affect several of the properties considered to be prerequisites for good auto-adhesion or building tack. Even though surfaces which are about to be laminated appear to be smooth, they are very rough when viewed on a molecular scale [11]. To develop the maximum amount of actual contact area, it is essential for the surfaces to have good flow properties under compression. Commercial carcass compounds, of either natural or SBR rubber are usually rather soft and meet this requirement quite well. However, the stock must not only flow well but stay put after the compressive force is relaxed. A common term associated with this phenomenon is "nerve." Natural rubber has more nerve than SBR and when softened with oil, tends to retain this nerve. Resins reduce the nerve of natural rubber and, thereby, contribute to good building tack by maintaining an increased area of actual contact of the stocks. SBR, on the other hand, tends to be rather plastic and doughy and with very little nerve by the time it reaches the calender. This is illustrated in Figure 5.

Once the surfaces are in contact, intermolecular diffusion must occur across the interface. However, Skewis [12] reports this is not really the limiting parameter of good building tack since the intermingling of polymer chains across an interface is very rapid.

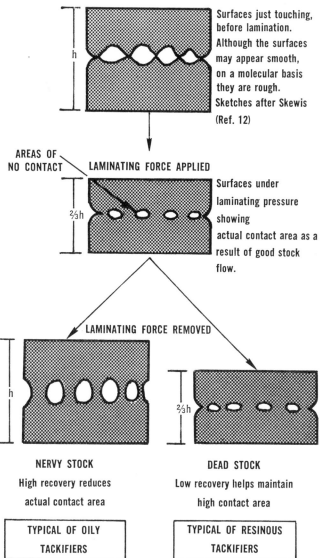

Fig. 5

EFFECT OF NERVE ON TACK (Natural Rubber)

Surfaces just touching, before lamination. Although the surfaces may appear smooth, on a molecular basis they are rough. Sketches after Skewis (Ref. 12)

AREAS OF NO CONTACT

LAMINATING FORCE APPLIED

Surfaces under laminating pressure showing actual contact area as a result of good stock flow.

LAMINATING FORCE REMOVED

NERVY STOCK
High recovery reduces actual contact area

TYPICAL OF OILY TACKIFIERS

DEAD STOCK
Low recovery helps maintain high contact area

TYPICAL OF RESINOUS TACKIFIERS

Finally, now that the surfaces are in contact and have "become as one," the stock must have a high yield strength (often referred to as green strength) or else the article may be delaminated very easily. Natural rubber is very good in this regard due, in part, to its ability to crystallize on extension. SBR and the polybutadienes are poor in this respect and as a result the addition of the relatively bulky, inflexible resin molecules improve green strength and, thereby, building tack.

Passenger tire body stocks are blends of natural and SBR, the natural rubber functioning as a tackifier. With resins to reduce the nerve of the natural and to increase the green strength of the SBR, compounders have found they can reduce the natural rubber content of such stocks, thereby improving the cost picture and minimizing the reversion tendency of the natural rubber.

In addition, much larger amounts of resinous tackifiers may be used in body stocks without resulting in overly soft, mushy compounds compared to liquid tackifiers.

Since resins have high glass transition temperatures, they can be used to raise the average T_g of a compound, a significant observation today as new elastomers are compared on the basis of their glass transition temperatures [13]. Only recently [14] has this effect been investigated and much more remains to be done. From both experience and theory, it is known that different resins have different effects. This is discussed more fully in the next section under the subject of Compatibility. However, the overall results of resin addition would be expected to increase the T_g of the mixture and, consequently, to be similar to the effects experienced by increasing the speed of testing or lowering the test temperature [15].

With these relationships in mind, a promising field of development lies in the use of resins in tread stocks. Of special significance is the wide variety of resins available today for testing. It should be possible to attain any degree of compatibility, or non-compatibility, desired. With the advent of solution polymers and with resins which are soluble in aliphatic solvents, it is now possible to use higher softening point resins by introducing them to the polymer before the removal of solvents. This makes available another parameter of resin difference and is one which would affect compatibility. While goals may vary, an important objective of resin addition to tread stocks would be to improve traction without lowering wear ratings.

24

Future research will be required to delineate more completely the type of performance which will be most improved by the addition of specific resins.

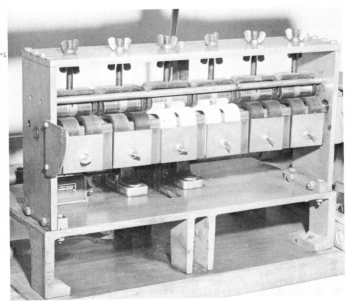

Ross Flex test — an important quality control and development test in the soling industry used as an indication of performance.

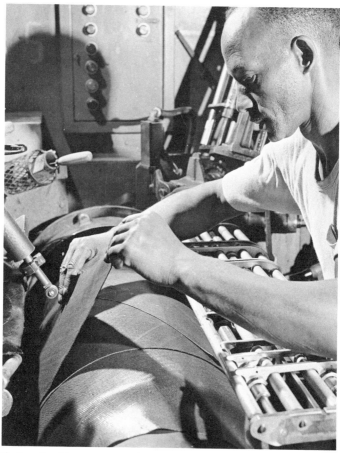

Photo of rubber compounder joining plies at a bias table cutter table in a tire manufacturing plant.

CHAPTER FOUR

HOW RESINS DIFFER

While rosin is a resin, all resins are not rosin. With this bit of profundity, an attempt will be made to relate resin differences to specific concerns, i.e., color, compatibility, stability and "observations not otherwise classified."

COLOR

Resins vary in color and, since this frequently reflects a degree of refining, color is often related to price, a not unimportant factor. The color of the resin naturally affects the cured color of the vulcanizate but the initial color of the resin can be quite misleading. Resins with equivalent original colors can vary widely in terms of the cured color of a light colored product. While the reasons have not been fully explored, certainly some of the gross differences are due to a dark reaction product of sulfur and resin. There is some indication the pH or metal content of mineral fillers may influence the color of the resin in the cured product.

Table 4 summarizes practical experience in the use of resins in light colored applications. Table 4A does the same thing but on a finer scale, reporting a measure of off-whiteness rather than the basic color of the product.

TABLE 4.
Type of Resin to Use in Colored Products

Product Color	Resins to Choose From
Whites and Pastels	Picco 6100-1-½, Picco N-100-1-½, Piccotex 100, Piccolyte
Oak	All above plus Picco N-100-2-½, Picco 100-3, Piccopale 100 SF
Tan	All above plus Piccodiene 2215 SRG
Browns and Reds	All above plus Resinex 100, Piccodiene 14215 SRG

Cured Color of a Resin Containing White SBR Stock

Resin	Cured Color, Blue reflectance values, the higher the number the whiter the color
Control, no resin	97
Piccotex 100	97
Picco N-100-1-½	90
Picco 6100-1-½	89
Picco 100-3	85
Piccopale 100 SF	75
Piccodiene 2215 SRG	68

The situation is somewhat different in regard to stain. Of course, staining is a relative matter. It makes a difference whether we are talking about migration stain, of concern on the skim stocks used in the body of white sidewall tires, or some manner of contact stain. While it is true that some resins stain more than others, from a practical standpoint, all of the PICCO resins except RESINEX can be considered nonstaining for tire use.

COMPATIBILITY

The degree of compatibility of a resin in a compound is a very important matter. However, it is a quality very difficult to measure in a meaningful way. It is even more difficult to relate any observations to precise, practical processing or cured vulcanizate properties.

It is frequently observed that mineral rubber (air blown asphalt) acts more like a filler than as a resin. This statement implies mineral rubber is not really soluble in the system involved, whereas, a resin is. If a resin is not compatible with an elastomer, it must grind up into a fine powder during the mixing operation. It is conceivable that each such finely divided, insoluble resin particle would act as a filler. Burke [16] has described the reinforcement of rubbers by organic fillers, especially the "vinylic fillers." He prepared masterbatches from SBR latices and polystyrene latex and compounded them both below and above the softening point of the polystyrene. Compounds prepared at temperatures below 90°C showed a limited reinforcing effect by the polystyrene but when prepared above 100°C, the reinforcing effect was lost. Burke concludes that to be reinforcing, the organic filler must remain in colloidal sized particles, insoluble in the elastomer. Thus, the heat softening of a resin during milling implies better dispersion of the resin in the rubber, regardless of solubility, than would be the case if the

28

resin had not "melted" during mixing but had dispersed by virtue of the grinding action of the elastomer on the brittle resin.

On the other hand, to speak of a resin which is soluble in an elastomer suggests that individual resin molecules are located between elastomer chains. For some reason, it is more common to speak of resins as having varying "solvency" powers on the elastomer. Since we are referring to relatively small amounts of resin, compared to the elastomer, the net effect is the same and is consistent with the usual view of a plasticizer [17].

A fascinating development has been the recent introduction of block copolymers with colloidal sized segments of one of the monomers. The properties described are frequently reminiscent of those which resin technologists attribute to a condition of "limited incompatibility." In any event, the analogy is not without merit as we seek to appreciate the variations that are possible as we blend resins and rubbers.

Obviously, between the extremes of plasticizer and filler, many intermediate situations are possible, in addition to the complications introduced by differentiating between reinforcing and nonreinforcing fillers. For practical purposes the word "reinforcing" has become the adjective used almost exclusively by the noun, carbon black. Resins, by and large, do not increase abrasion and modulus, key objectives in Parkinsons definition of reinforcement [19]. Although Burke [18] classifies coumarone indene resins as nonreinforcing by Parkinsons rule, hose and soling compounders commonly speak of them as reinforcing resins since they do reinforce tensile and flex resistance, paramount properties of their products.

The age-old method of measuring compatibility is to dissolve both materials in a mutual solvent and cast a film on glass. A compatible system gives a clear film while incompatibility results in an opaque film. A further refinement of this method is to examine the film with a phase microscope. Unfortunately, this does not always serve to explain the differences observed by rubber compounding. A mixture of 30 parts of PICCOPALE 100 SF resin in 100 parts of SBR 1502 gives a perfectly clear film but from past experience we would expect the resin to migrate to the surface, a practical result of incompatibility. The refractive index of both of these ingredients is nearly the same and, under these circumstances, it would be very difficult to see undissolved particles of the resin.

Hock and coworkers have devised a method of detecting surface irregularities indicating incompatibility [20]. This work has been most illuminating in understanding pressure sensitive adhesives, but their techniques for producing electron microphotographs is rather sophisticated for most laboratories.

To dissolve a resin in a medium requires a similarity of attractive forces between the resin and solvent compared to the attractive interactions between individual resin molecules and individual solvent molecules [21]. Over the past several years a system of predicting solubility has evolved on the basis of the forces required to separate molecules, as is done when a liquid is vaporized [22]. Using solvents of varying solubility parameters and hydrogen bonding indices, it is possible to determine the solubility parameter of a resin and a rubber. On this basis, when two materials have very similar solubility parameter values they should be compatible. This system works for resins in liquid solvents [23] and for blends of elastomers [8]. It is expected that this system is generally valid even for two materials of such widely different molecular weights as a resin and an elastomer. However, there is some indication the measurement may be too coarse to aid in the prediction of resin rubber blend properties. A notable "for instance" lies in a comparison of the two resins, PICCOLYTE S-100 (beta pinene) and PICCOLYTE Alpha 115. If we assume the development of pressure sensitive tack has something to do with compatibility—then it can only be frustrating to recognize both resins have virtually the same solubility parameters, yet one tackifies SBR and one doesn't. It seems apparent we are trying to perform an appendectomy with an axe; we need even more sophisticated tools with which to "operate."

As a matter of interest, the solubility parameter values for several resins and rubbers are reported in Table 5.

TABLE 5.
Solubility Parameters of Rubbers and Resins

Rubbers (Ref. 8)		Resins (Ref. 23) values reported are at 2.5 (low) hydrogen bonding index		
			range	midpoint
Polybutadiene	8.17 to 8.22	Piccolyte A115	6.9-9.8	8.4
SBR 1500	8.13	Piccolyte S100	7.0-9.8	8.4
Natural Rubber	8.25	Piccotex 100	6.9-11.0	9.0
Neoprene GNA	9.26	Picco L30-2	7.0-10.5	8.8
Butyl Rubber	7.6	Piccopale 100	6.9-9.7	8.3
ERP (50 molar % Ethylene)	7.88	Piccoplastic A75	7.2-10.9	9.1
		Picco N-100-1	7.8-11.1	9.5
		Picco N-100-2½	8.1-11.6	9.9
		Picco 6110-1½	6.9-11.2	9.1

Compatibility has recently been defined by the measurement of glass transition temperatures [8]. Blends of elastomers exhibiting two or more second order transition points are said to be incompatible. A compatible blend is defined as one which has only one glass transition temperature, it being of intermediate value. If the purpose of the blending is to achieve a mixture exhibiting some of the properties of **both** individual components, it is important that they are not fully compatible [27]. If the object is to obtain results representing an average of the two components, compatible materials should be used.

An interesting example of this is contained in the stress strain data published by the Shell Chemical Co., using blends of KRATON 101* (a block copolymer of butadiene and styrene which does not require curing) and a variety of resins [24]. Figure 6 shows typical stress strain curves when the elastomer, KRATON 101, is compounded with 50 phr of an aromatic and an aliphatic resin. The blend using an aromatic coumarone indene resin shows a high modulus at low elongation, typical of a resin, and the high tensile strength typical of the uncompounded elastomer. The results with an aliphatic trepene resin indicate that it is completely compatible with the KRATON 101 elastomer. In this particular case it is not really sufficient to talk about whether or not the resin is compatible with the rubber, but we must define which part of the elastomer chain we are talking about as being compatible.

Until more such measurements are made on resin containing compounds, we must content ourselves with making judgments based on past experience and by the ancient guideline, "like

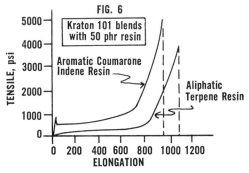

FIG. 6

Kraton 101 blends with 50 phr resin

Aromatic Coumarone Indene Resin

Aliphatic Terpene Resin

TENSILE, psi
ELONGATION

*KRATON is the registered trademark of the Shell Chemical Co. for a new elastomer requiring no vulcanization.

31

dissolves like." This is essentially what we have been saying above in a little more specific and somewhat more complex manner.

Aromatic vs. Aliphatic Resins

To use the guideline, "like dissolves like," one must know more about what resins are "like." Two principal tests have been used for this purpose, the Cloud Point and the Aniline Point tests. The Cloud Point test measures the compatibility of a resin with mineral oil, a very paraffinic substance. The value reported is the temperature at which a specified mixture of the two will give a cloudy appearance, having been cooled from a temperature at which the liquid mixture was clear. The Aniline Point test is much the same but the solvent is aniline, a very polar material. Table 6 indicates the very wide range of aniline points available in the Picco family of hydrocarbon resins.

TABLE 6.
Aniline Point Ranges of Hydrocarbon Resins

Class	Names	Aniline Point Range
Aromatic	Picco N-100-2-½ Picco 100-3 Picco 6100-1-½ Resinex, Piccotex	$+15°C$ to under $-30°C$
Intermediate Aromaticity	Piccodiene Series	about $+50°C$
Non Aromatic (Aliphatic)	Piccopale 100 SF, Piccolyte A & S series	100°C and over

One inherent deficiency of these tests is that small amounts of high molecular weight material or highly paraffinic components will tend to precipitate first and obscure the chemical differences we seek to observe. Nevertheless, these tests do give usable information when coupled with molecular weight distribution data and what is known about chemical composition [25]. In Table 7 resins have been separated into three rough classes, i.e., aromatic, intermediate aromatic and non aromatic. Although the method parallels the familiar grouping of process oils as aromatic, naphthenic and paraffinic, it should not be assumed that all of the performance characteristics of oils which are attributed to their aromaticity can be extrapolated to give us guidelines in the use of resins.

TABLE 7.
Resin-Elastomer Compatibilities

Hydrocarbon Resin Class	Natural Rubber	SBR	Neoprene	Nitrile
AROMATIC (Picco 6100-1-½)	OK	OK	OK	OK
INTERMEDIATE AROMATICITY (Piccodiene Series)	OK	OK	?	NO
NON AROMATIC (Piccopale 100 SF)	OK	?	NO	NO

Table 7 is a simple tabulation of the years of experience of people using these resins and conforms to the principle "like dissolves like." The question marks indicate that sometimes a particular blend will "work" and sometimes not, no doubt a function of the other compounding ingredients in the mixture, or simply the level at which the resin is used.

The same field experience is the basis for Table 8. Sales experience indicates the "aromaticity" of a resin is important and is the controlling factor in determining compatibility.

TABLE 8.
RESIN COLOR

	RESIN TYPE	COAL TAR O T
Resins below this line are used for tack in carcass stocks and adhesives ⬇	AROMATIC	Piccotex 10 Picco N-10C
	INTERMEDIATE	
Resins above this line ⬆ are used in mineral loaded stocks	NON AROMATIC	Piccolyte S1 Piccolyte A

Effect on Applications

Aromatic resins (such as PICCO 6100-1-½) are used in mineral loaded stocks for the "organic reinforcement" effect noted earlier. Of course, it must be remembered that most mineral filled, light colored stocks are made with SBR or neoprene. One would expect the aromatic resins to have the best compatibility with these polymers.

The resins with substantial aliphatic content (PICCOPALE and PICCOLYTE) are the ones used as tackifiers in carcass stocks and adhesives. Again we must remember that at least some natural rubber is used in the overwhelming majority of such stocks. Natural rubber, when properly tackified, is an excellent tackifier for SBR. One would expect aliphatic resins to be more compatible with natural rubber than the aromatic resins.

On the other hand, there is reason to believe complete compatibility is not always desirable [20, 24]. Resins have been known to bloom and many chemists feel this is good, especially those working on tackifiers. Certainly Hock and coworkers [20] feel a certain amount of incompatibility is essential in the development of good properties for pressure sensitive tape.

Bussemaker in his 1964 Rubber Reviews [26] paper, covered the subject of tack in rubber. Table 9 is reproduced from that paper and is the previously unpublished data of van Rossem which he gave at the International Meeting in Cleveland in 1950.

The results illustrate the wide variation that can be expected in the testing of tackifiers. To the author's knowledge, it is not common to use 100% SBR compounds in building operations without the use of cements. It is difficult therefore to speak from experience on the tackifying of such stocks. Aromatic resins are

COAL TAR 1-5	COAL TAR 7-14	COAL TAR 18-22
Picco 6100-1½ Picco 100-3 Picco N-100-2½		Resinex 100
Piccodiene 2215 SRG	Piccodiene 14215 SRG	
Piccopale 100 SF		

TABLE 9.

Effect of 10 Parts of Tackifier on the Tack of an SBR Compound with 44 Parts of EPC Black

Tackifier	Plasticity, Hoekstra	Tack kg/cm^2
————	57	0.15
Cumarone resin	55	0.15
Staybelite resin	47	0.15
Staybelite ester	54	0.15
Hercolyn	41	0.20
Pine tar	41	0.25
Rosin	46	0.25
Rosin ester B	44	0.25
Rosin ester P	51	0.30
Rosin oil	35	0.35
Machine oil	37	0.35
Pentalyn A	45	0.45
Pentalyn H	45	0.50
Koresin	42	0.85
Piccolyte S 115	66	0.85
Piccolyte S 100	69	0.80
Piccolyte S 85	44	1.00

* Stabelite, Hercolyn and Pentalyn are the registered trademarks of the Hercules Powder Company for modified rosins.
Koresin is the registered trademark of the General Aniline Co. for a condensation product of butylphenol and acetylene.

commonly used to keep highly loaded SBR stocks from bagging on the mill or calender, but PICCOPALE, a non aromatic resin, works well too. Hot tack can be achieved for orbit tread stocks by the use of PICCOPALE 100 SF, PICCODIENE 14215 SRG and PICCO 6100-1½ resins, the complete range of the available aromatic content variations and this makes it difficult to predict what a compounder should try first. Judging from many contacts with compounders who are evaluating tackifiers, a very great deal depends on the polymer system involved.

To complete our analysis of resin use as a function of aromaticity, the resins with an intermediate amount of aromatic content (PICCODIENE Series) perform well in both types of applications, i.e., they give the reinforcement effect of the aromatic resins and the tackifying effect of the non aromatic resins.

Table 8 demonstrates that all the resins in a horizontal row compete with each other for the same applications, the final choice being largely a matter of color requirements. Resin advertising sometimes gives the impression that all resins are good for all things. This is why.

A complicating factor in the prediction of compatibilty is molecular weight and molecular weight distribution [25]. While high molecular weights in resins are related to increased modulus and hardness in the vulcanizate, the same quality generally lessens the compatibility of a resin in an elastomer. The cloud point test is the one most commonly used to indicate this resin characteristic. Resins exhibiting a cloud point of above 0°C are the ones offering a slight increase in modulus and hardness and impart a leathery feel to the vulcanizate. Most of the resins used in rubber compounding today do not exhibit the cloud point effect except at very low temperatures. These are sometimes referred to as "soluble" resins. Over the years, the industry has moved from cloud point resins to the less expensive "soluble" resins. This gradual change is virtually completed now and indicates the virtues of the cloud point resins are not great enough to warrant their extra cost. Not to be confused with cloud point, the aniline point test still serves a useful purpose as a means of differentiating between aromatic and non-aromatic resins.

STABILITY

The choice of a particular resin is important as it affects:

1. Cure rate.
2. Drying out of tackified surfaces by oxidation.
3. Aged physicals.
4. Afteryellowing and ultraviolet resistance of light colored products.

Perhaps without justification, most of the discussion about the effect of resin on these qualities has centered on tests for unsaturation. In addition, rosin acids can retard cure and the hydroxyl groups in phenolic resins can affect the cure rate but these resin types are not the major concern of this paper.

Many tests which measure unsaturation do not always correrate. For instance, PICCOPALE resin has a higher Hanus Iodine Number than PICCODIENE resin, indicating a greater "reactivity" for the former. Yet, stocks containing PICCODIENE resin are slower curing. The Electrometric Bromine Number test correctly shows the PICCODIENE resin to be more reactive. The complicating factor in this instance is that PICCOPALE polymer contains tertiary hydrogen and the halogens combine by substitution as well as by addition to a double bond. In addition, it is not entirely logical that unsaturation in the resin should inhibit cure in view of the much greater unsaturation in most base polymers.

Obviously, the reactivity of a resin with a halogen does not necessarily allow us to predict the reactivity of the resin with curatives or oxygen. The Naval Stores industry has frequently compared rosin with its derivatives by studying the oxygen absorption properties of the resin. Working with PICCO rubber processing resins, we have become accustomed to believing none of the unsaturation tests are dependable predictors, except when they happen to correspond to field results.

From the standpoint of experience, all of the PICCO resins except PICCODIENE can be considered as non-reactive in terms of cure rate. PICCOPALE resin is outstanding by its relative inertness and large amounts may be used without any curative adjustments except that made for the normal dilution effect. This property has been especially useful at plants operating on the borderline of good tire building tack. It has been possible to add extra tackifier to handle problems, such as separation in the bead turnup area, without also having to make curative adjustments.

Center sample contains hydrocarbon resin. All others contain rosin or rosin derivatives. Note differences in surface degradation after aging for 24 months. Hydrocarbon resin surface still tacky and "live." All others cracked and hard.

PICCOLYTE resin, derived from a terpene, has been used in pressure sensitive adhesives for many years. PICCOLYTE resin is considered as outstanding in regard to its resistance to the ravages of time when used in tapes and adhesives. PICCOPALE resin enjoys the same reputation when used in skim stocks. Calendered stocks maintain good building tack for a longer period when it is used in place of comparably priced rosin derivatives. In addition, compounders have said the PICCOPALE resin gives a more uniform building tack without the variations in summer and winter weather that they have experienced with other systems. Oddly enough, PICCODIENE resin seems to do quite well in this respect despite its generally reactive nature. Most users however, do feel PICCOPALE resin gives more tack and certainly does so with less effect on cure rate.

From what has been said, one would tend to ascribe the superior aging performance of the PICCOLYTE resin to the low degree of unsaturation in this resin. However, when the resins PICCOLYTE and PICCOPALE, both excellent tackifiers for natural rubber, are hydrogenated to reduce their natural unsaturation, they lose their tack inducing capabilities. While this may reflect some subtle change in compatibility, it does seem apparent that a small amount of oxygen susceptibility is important for tack induction but too much may cause premature loss of tack.

Some consumers have reported resins help maintain good aged physicals, compared to oils. This may be due to the lower volatility of the resin. Other than this observation, no pattern of correlation of aged physicals has been established with unsaturation measurements. When PICCODIENE resin was first developed, it was expected that it would give poor aging properties due to its higher unsaturation. This has not been the case and thereby demonstrates the pitfalls when making extrapolations from one group of compounding ingredients to another.

Compounders frequently report PICCOPALE resin in carcass stocks give better aged physicals, compared to the use of oils or liquid tackifiers. More recently there have been indications that other resins such as PICCODIENE 14215SRG and PICCO 6100-1½ are even better. Although the reasons for such behaviour are not understood, the time has come for a more extensive comparison of oils and resins, both as processing aids and as extenders.

Coal derived coumarone indene resins produce excellent light colored products but have always been known to afteryellow under the influence of ultraviolet light. Some of the petroleum equivalents (PICCO 6100-1½) of these resins are more stable in this respect.

The aliphatic resins are completely compatible with wax and are frequently used, in other industries, to toughen wax films. Perhaps for this reason, PICCOPALE resin is sometimes used to improve the weathering resistance for wax protected compounds.

OBSERVATIONS NOT OTHERWISE CLASSIFIED

Hot Melt Viscosity

An examination of solution and hot melt viscosities is of interest as we seek to deduce micro differences in resins from their bulk properties. For instance, the hot melt viscosity of molten PICCOPALE 100 resin is greater than that of a coumarone indene resin with the same ball and ring softening point. Further information is available in the appendix but for purposes of illustration, the values for these two resins are recorded below.

TABLE 10.
Hot Melt Viscosities

	Picco N-100-1½ (Coumarone-Indene)	Piccopale 100 (Aliphatic pet. resin)
Softening Point Ball and Ring, °C.	100	100
Viscosity, Poise		
at 150°C	8	80
at 160°C	4	32
at 170°C	2	18
at 180°C	1	8
Mol. Wgt. by freezing point depression		
Whole Resin	700	1200
Major Fractions by non solvent precipitation	500-2400	850-1500

It is generally agreed that for low molecular weight hydrocarbon resins, the hot melt viscosity above 160°C. is influenced mostly by molecular weight as opposed to structural considerations. The results observed are in agreement, qualitatively at least, with molecular weight determinations based on freezing point depressions in benzene. Although the resins selected for illustration have divergent hot melt viscosities, at 100°C. each has approximately the same viscosity by definition of the ball and ring softening point determination. It is not unreasonable then to regard this as a crossover point, as we extrapolate backwards, from the easily measured hot melt viscosities, through the ball and ring point, to the 10^{13} poise value each resin again holds in common in the glassy condition. The net effect would be to produce a curve of the general shape as in Figure 7.

At 100°C. one would expect the structure of the resin to play an important part in determining the melt viscosity in addition to the molecular weight effect. From what we know of the chemical structure of the two resins (pp. 3, 10), PICCOPALE resin has more opportunities for bond rotation and one would therefore predict a lower glass transition temperature for this resin because of this greater flexibility in the chain. While the fragmentary data available does not confirm this prediction, a more flexible structure for PICCOPALE resin is suggested by the fact that a higher molecular weight is required for this resin to achieve a 100°C. softening point. More work of this type is required to delineate more clearly the upper part (below 100°C.) of the extrapolation in Figure 7.

It is difficult to prescribe precise significance to the observation that PICCOPALE resin has a more flexible structure than other resins or even to the fact it has a relatively narrow range of molecular weight distribution. But where exact meanings are lacking, there is room for "intuitive" compounding.

It is essential for processing that some sort of low molecular weight fraction be present in a commercial formulation. It may derive from the low molecular weight polymer in the rubber itself or, from oils or resins added to the composition. It is interesting to compare each of these in some important properties.

TABLE 11.
A Comparison of Low Molecular Weight Substances

	OILS	RESINS	RUBBERS (low MW fraction)
Flexibility	Excellent	Poor	Excellent
Hardness Effect Green Strength	Poor	Excellent	Fair
Modulus	Poor	Fair	Excellent
Permanence (Aging)	Fair	Excellent	Excellent
Cost	Low	Moderate	High

FIGURE 7.

Effect of Resin Structure on Molten Viscosity

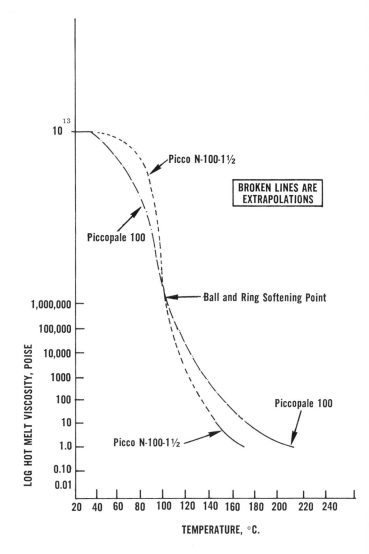

42

Of course, no rubber processing resin really approaches the flexibility of a rubber molecule. However, PICCOPALE resin, with a somewhat more flexible structure than other resins could be expected to respond to shock and molecular movement better than other resins. It should act less like a hard, inflexible lump and more like a rubber. To use the non-precise language of intuition, a flexible resin would be expected to be "more cooperative" when used with a rubber. The most widely used rubber processing resin today is PICCOPALE, and there are those who feel this is because of the very point under discussion.

Solution Viscosity

TABLE 12.
Resin Solution Viscosities

	Picco N-100-1½ (Coumarone-Indene)	Piccopale 100 (Aliphatic pet. resin)
Viscosity, Poise 70% soln., 25°C.		
In Toluene	4	8
In Mineral Spirits	40	22

When toluene is used as the solvent, the viscosity relationships of the two resins are reasonable in view of the higher molecular weight of the PICCOPALE polymer. When mineral spirits is used as the solvent, the relationship is reversed. This phenomenon is well known in the protective coatings field. It is not unusual to experience an increase in solution viscosity as the system approaches a condition of non-solvency. One is tempted to draw the analogy that aromatic oils do not decrease the Mooney of oil extended SBR as much as aliphatic oils. PICCOPALE resin does lower the Mooney of natural rubber more than an aromatic resin but, in SBR, they both act alike. At the present time it is impossible to ascribe specific rubber compounding significance to these observations but, if we are interested in how resins differ, this is a case in point.

Soft Resins

While 100°C. softening point resins are the most commonly used, lower softening point resins are frequently needed. Mill mixed stocks, especially low quality ones, sometimes will not develop enough heat to flux a resin over 75°C. softening point. For the same reason, very soft compounds often require a 10° or 25°C. resin. The softening point of the resin has an effect on the softness of the legs in an adhesive bond (harshness) and PICCOPALE 70SF resin (70°C. softening point) is sometimes preferred over PICCOPALE 100 SF grade for this reason.

Resins with ball and ring softening points below 100°C. cannot be flaked due to remassing problems. Most compounders find the convenience of handling a flaked resin overides any minor effect on processing attributed to a lower softening point resin. One of the major drawbacks to many of the rosin derivatives is the simple fact most of them cannot be flaked.

Cloud Points

Resins with Cloud points below 0°C. are known as soluble resins. They are soluble in very aliphatic solvents and are mutually compatible with rubber processing oils. It has not been demonstrated but it would be expected that migrating oil would cause resin to migrate also, if the resin is oil soluble. High concentrations of resins are sometimes used at interfaces, in a splice cement for instance, and it would seem preferable to have the resin diffuse to adjoining areas after cure.

Specific Gravity

Resins also vary in specific gravity. Low gravity resins like PICCOPALE 100 SF enjoy a bulking advantage of about 20% compared to the aromatic resins. Obviously, resins are generally chosen because they "work" and not because of their bulking advantage. Once in a while however, this is the characteristic that tips the scale, particularly when the product is sold on a volumetric or "per piece" basis.

CHAPTER FIVE

RESIN DATA

RESIN MANUFACTURING

The polymerization of hydrocarbon resins is generally an exothermic reaction. The monomers are usually dissolved in an inert solvent to control the rate of the exotherm. In the case of coal tar resins the monomers are available in a fraction from the coke oven byproduct operations known as light oil. In other instances it is necessary to add the inert diluent separately.

Chilled brine is used to remove the heat of reaction and to attain a low reaction temperature. There is much demand for resins of a pale color. This is controlled largely by the condition of the raw materials, the reaction temperature and protection from thermal and oxidative degredation after the resin has been formed.

The catalyst is generally of the Lewis acid type and is removed by a washing operation.

The inert solvent diluent and low molecular weight resin is removed by a high vacuum distillation. Sometimes this is aided by the addition of a little steam. For relatively minor differences in the softening point of the finished resin, it is possible to control this by the quantity of low molecular weight resin (dimers and trimers) left in the resin during the distillation step.

The molten resin, after quality control procedures, is flaked or cast in drums or bags.

Where the volume throughput has justified it, operations have been converted to a continuous system allowing the use of control instrumentation. Molten resin is protected by a blanket of inert gas wherever possible.

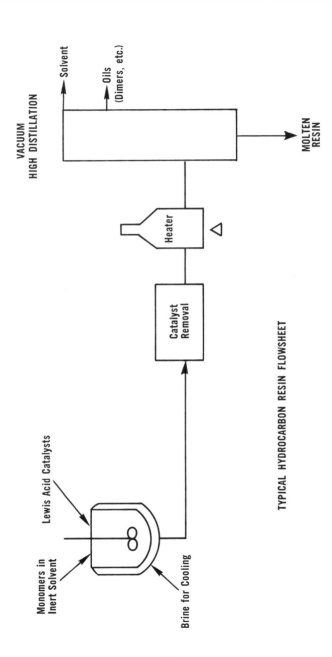

TYPICAL HYDROCARBON RESIN FLOWSHEET

Solvent

Oils
(Dimers, etc.)

VACUUM
HIGH DISTILLATION

MOLTEN
RESIN

Heater

Catalyst
Removal

Lewis Acid Catalysts

Monomers in
Inert Solvent

Brine for Cooling

MOLECULAR WEIGHT DISTRIBUTION

Several of the Picco resins have been examined for molecular weight distribution. It is convenient to separate fractions of varying molecular weight by partial precipitation, i.e., adding a non solvent to a solution of the resin. The results reported represent an examination of each of several fractions for a variety of properties.

POLYMER DISTRIBUTION OF PICCO N-100-1 RESIN

	Whole resin	Fractions 1	2	3	4	5
Per cent by wt.	100	37.2	21.0	12.0	18.0	11.8
Softening pt., C° (ball & ring)	102	38.5	97.0	144.0	188.0	210.0
Intrinsic viscosity	0.048	0.026	0.034	0.049	0.050	0.073
Cloud point, C°	64	<0	<0	<0	126	169
Molecular weight (cryoscopic)	733	507		997		2392

POLYMER DISTRIBUTION OF PICCO 110-3 RESIN

		Fraction 1	2	3	4	5	6	7	8	9	10
Whole resin											
Wt., per cent	100	7.9	12.1	10.1	10.3	8.8	9.0	11.7	11.9	8.8	9.4
Softening pt. (ASTM E 28)	110	54.5	64.5	86.0	91.5	101	102	103	110	133	149.5
Molecular wt.	973	582	------	------	828	------	892	------	1042	1270	1300
Refractive index	1.575				1.582		1.584		1.585		1.591
Intrinsic viscosity		0.024	0.025	0.028	0.028	0.032	0.035	0.036	0.039	0.044	0.056

POLYMER DISTRIBUTION OF PICCOPALE RESIN

	Whole resin	Fraction 1	2	3	4
Per cent of resin	100	20	28	20	31
Softening point	103	123	112	110	77
Density at 20° C	0.98	0.99	0.98	0.97	0.96
Refractive index, 20° C	1.53	1.539	1.533	1.531	1.521
Intrinsic viscosity	0.04	0.044	0.041	0.04	0.03
Cryoscopic mol. wt.	1200	1500	1350	1200	870

POLYMER DISTRIBUTION OF PICCOLYTE S115 RESIN

	Fraction 1	2	3	4	5	6
Per cent of resin	21.8	14.8	13.8	14.7	13.9	16.7
Softening point, C°	147.5	146.5	145.0	134	115	76
Density, 20° C	1.00	0.995	0.987	0.983	0.970	0.940
Av. mol. cryoscopic wt.	2190			1125		552
Intrinsic viscosity	0.058	0.056	0.047	0.047		0.03

ANILINE POINTS

For hydrocarbon resins the following aniline point and mixed aniline point procedures are used:

1. *Aniline Point (A.P.)* (see note 1 below).

The procedure is identical with that of A.S.T.M. D-611-51T except that 10.0 grams of resin is used instead of the specified 10.0 ml. of oil sample.

2. *Mixed Aniline Point (M.A.P.).*

The procedure is identical with that of A.S.T.M. D-611-51T except that:

   a. 5.0 ml. of *methylcyclohexane* (A.P. = 39.9°C., see note 2) is substituted for 5.0 ml. of n-heptane.

   b. 5.0 *grams of resin* is used instead of 5.0 ml. of sample.

   c. The value obtained is designated *"M. M.A.P."*

   d. From the value of M. M.A.P., using Fig. 8, the equivalent resin aniline point (A.P.) is read.

Additional Notes and Instructions

1. If a determined resin straight aniline point is lower than the softening point of the resin, the value is regarded as invalid and is not to be reported. The M. M.A.P. method should be used.

2. Fig. 8 is based on methylcyclohexane having a determined A.P. of 39.9°C. If the aniline point of the methylcyclohexane used in a given test differs from 39.9°C., the observed M. M.A.P. is to be corrected by one-half the difference before using Fig. 1 to read the equivalent A.P.

FIGURE 8.

STRAIGHT vs. MIXED ANILINE POINT
OIL & RESIN SAMPLES
METHYLCYCLOHEXANE DILUENT

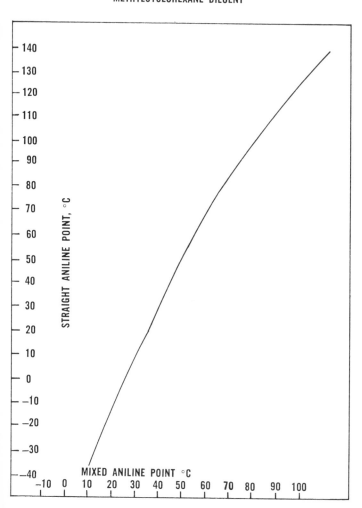

Color of resin used as reinforcing agent becomes very important in compounding for light-colored products. Color of hydrocarbon resins ranges from water-white to black through an amber tint. Cured color must be watched closely.

Color Conversion Chart

COLOR CONVERSION CHART

This method of color comparison should give useful information. However, it should be pointed out that the colors are approximate. Comparisons are complicated by trying to examine varying degrees of yellowness or redness.

Coal Tar*	Gardner**	Rosin**
½	5	Y
—	6-7	X
—	6-7	WW
1	7-8	WG
—	8-9	N
1½	9-10	M
2	11	K
2½	12-13	G
3	14	F
4	16	E
5	> 18	D

*Picco Laboratory Method 1

**Henry A. Gardner and G. G. Sward, Physical and Chemical Examination of Paints, Varnishes, Lacquers, and Colors, Bethesda, Md. (1950), Henry A. Gardner Laboratory, Inc., p. 102.

BALL AND RING SOFTENING POINT

The ball and ring softening point is a standard test used on hydrocarbon resins. If your laboratory is accustomed to running a lot of these tests, there is nothing to it. However, if you only run a few, sometimes it is difficult to get good agreement with the results supplied by the resin manufacturer.

Usually, any differences are resolved by a very strict adherence to the rate of heating, but even seemingly minor deviations from the specification, such as the size of the glass vessel, do make a difference. The problem is that the viscosity of the resin is changing very quickly and the test reports the temperature at which the viscosity of the resin will allow the steel ball to fall one inch. In a way, it's like trying to shoot a bird on the wing from a moving car. Sometimes solution viscosity measurements or a hot melt viscosity is substituted for the ball and ring method.

It is important to avoid overheating of the resin sample prior to pouring it in the mold, i.e., not over 40°C over the expected softening point. Although the glycerine is not stirred, it is customary to place the source of heat to one side of the center of the beaker to encourage good convection.

51

PICCO Lab Method No. 6 is included for the guidance of those experiencing problems with this test.

SOFTENING POINT OF RESINS BY RING AND BALL METHOD
Modified from ASTM E-28

SCOPE

1. This method of test describes a procedure for the determination of the softening point of resins by means of a ring and ball apparatus.

SOFTENING POINT

2. (a) In general, with materials of this type, softening does not take place at a definite temperature. As the temperature rises, these materials gradually and imperceptibly change from brittle or exceedingly thick and slow-flowing materials to softer and less viscous liquids. For this reason, the determination of the softening point must be made by a fixed, arbitrary, and closely defined method if the results obtained are to be comparable.

   (b) In this method, the softening point is defined as the temperature at which a disk of the sample held within a horizontal ring is forced downward a distance of 1 in. under the weight of a steel ball as the sample is heated at a prescribed rate in a water or glycerine bath.

APPARATUS

3. The apparatus shall consist of the following:

   (a) Ring—A brass-shouldered ring conforming to the dimensions shown in Fig. 1 (a).

   (a) Ball—A steel ball, 9.53 mm (3/8 in.) in diameter, weighing between 3.45 and 3.55 g.

   (c) Ball Centering Guide—A guide for centering the ball, constructed of brass and having the general shape and dimensions illustrated in Fig. 1 (c), the use of which is optional.

   (d) Container—A glass vessel, capable of being heated, not less than 8.5 cm (3.5 in.) in diameter and not less than 12.7 cm (5 in.) in depth from the bottom of the flare. (An 800-ml low-form Griffin Beaker of heat-resistant glass meets this requirement.)

   (e) (1) When using apparatus shown in Fig. 1 (d) : Bottom of ring shall be 1.0 in. above the horizontal plate below it; bottom surface of the horizontal plate shall be at least 0.5 and not more than 0.75 in. above the bottom

52

of the beaker; and depth of liquid in the beaker shall be not less than 4.0 in.

(2) Thermometer shall be suspended so that the bottom of the bulb is level with the bottom of the ring and within 0.5 in. but not touching the ring.

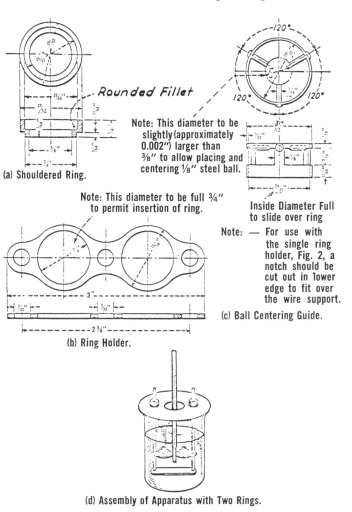

Rounded Fillet

(a) Shouldered Ring.

Note: This diameter to be slightly (approximately 0.002″) larger than ⅜″ to allow placing and centering ⅛″ steel ball.

Note: This diameter to be full ¾″ to permit insertion of ring.

Inside Diameter Full to slide over ring

Note: — For use with the single ring holder, Fig. 2, a notch should be cut out in lower edge to fit over the wire support.

(c) Ball Centering Guide.

(b) Ring Holder.

(d) Assembly of Apparatus with Two Rings.

Fig. 1.—Shouldered Ring, Ring Holder, Ball-Centering Guide, and Assembly of Apparatus Showing Two Rings.

METHOD OF TEST FOR SOFTENING POINT BY RING AND BALL APPARATUS

(f) Thermometers—An ASTM Low Softening Point Thermometer, having a range of —2 to +80 C, or +30 to +180 F, and conforming to the requirements for thermometer 15°C or 15°F as prescribed in the Standard Specifications for ASTM Thermometers. This is essentially an accurate total immersion thermometer graduated in either .2°C or .5°F.

An ASTM High Softening Point Thermometer, having a range of 30 to 200 C, or 85 to 392 F, and conforming to the sample while stirring thoroughly, but do not heat to a a total immersion thermometer graduated in either .5°C or 1°F.

Preparation of Sample

4. Pour Method:

Select a sample representative of the material under test. Melt the sample while stirring thoroughly, but do not heat to a temperature more than 100 F above its softening point. Avoid incorporating air bubbles in the mass. Immediately before filling the rings, preheat them to approximately the temperature at which the material is to be poured. Pour the sample into the ring so as to leave an excess on cooling. The ring, while being filled, should rest on a brass plate. After cooling for a minimum of 30 min., cut the excess material off cleanly with a slightly heated knife or spatula. Proceed with the test within 4 hours.

Procedure for Materials Having Softening Points 80 C (176 F) or Below

5. (a) Assembly of Apparatus—Fill the glass vessel, to a depth of not less than 4.0 and not more than 4.25 in., with freshly boiled distilled water which has been cooled to not less than 45 C (81 F) below the anticipated softening point, but in no case lower than 5 C (41 F). Unless the ball-centering guide is to be used, make a slight indentation in the center of the sample by pressing the ball or a rounded rod, slightly heated for hard materials, into the material at this point. Suspend the ring containing the sample in the water so that the lower horizontal plate (Fig. 1 (d), which is at least 0.5 in. and not more than 0.75 in. above the bottom of glass vessel. Suspend and

Standard laboratory set-up for determining ball-and-ring softening point of hydrocarbon resins.

ASTM low-softening-point thermometer so that the bottom of its bulb is level with the bottom of the ring, and within 0.5 in. but not touching the ring. Place the ball in the center of the upper surface of the material in the ring.

(b) Heating—Apply heat in such a manner that the temperature of the water is raised 5 C, or 10 F, per min. Avoid the effect of drafts, using shields if necessary.

(c) Permissible Variation in Rise of Temperature—The rate of rise of temperature shall be uniform and shall not be averaged over the period of the test. The maximum permissible variation for any minute period after the first three shall be $\pm$ 0.5 C or $\pm$ 1 F. Reject all tests in which the rate of rise exceeds these limits.

(d) Softening Point—Record as the softening point the temperature of the thermometer at the instant the material touches the lower horizontal plate. (Fig. 1 (d). Make no correction for the emergent stem of the thermometer.

PROCEDURE FOR MATERIALS HAVING SOFTENING POINTS ABOVE 80 C (176 F)

6. Use the same procedure as described in Section 5, except fill the bath with glycerine (Note) and use an ASTM high-softening-point thermometer. Use glycerine which has been cooled to not less than 45 C (81 F) below the anticipated softening point, but in no case lower than 35 C (95 F).

Note—For materials softening around 80 C (176 F) report the nature of the bath, whether water or glycerine, since a glycerine bath yields slightly higher results than a water bath.

PRECAUTIONS

7. The use of freshly boiled distilled water is essential, as otherwise air bubbles may form on the specimen and affect the result. Rigid adherence to the prescribed rate of heating is absolutely essential for reproducibility of results.

SOLUTION VISCOSITY DATA

Solution Viscosity Data are useful as we seek to deduce differences in the molecular weight and structure of resins from easily measured physical characteristics.

For convenience, they are gathered together on the following pages.

AROMATIC RESINS (COUMARONE-INDENE)
PICCO N SERIES

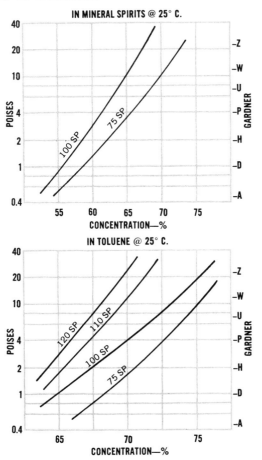

IN MINERAL SPIRITS @ 25° C.

IN TOLUENE @ 25° C.

PICCO 100 SERIES

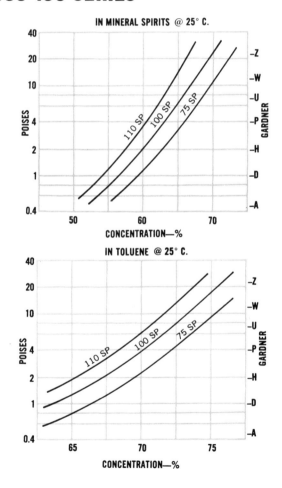

PICCO 6000 SERIES

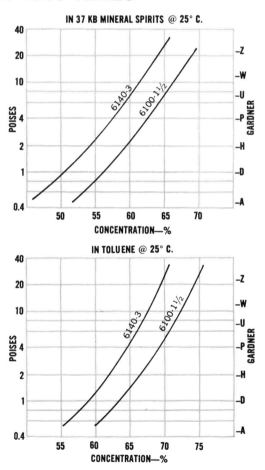

Solution Viscosities

PICCOPALE

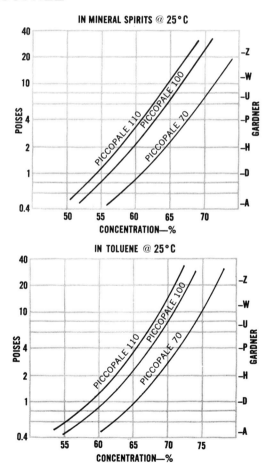

PICCODIENE

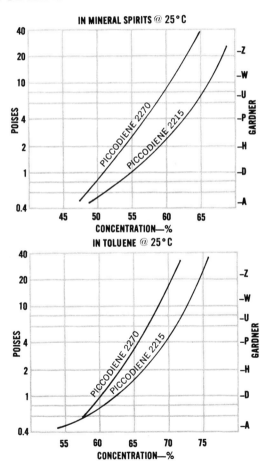

Solution Viscosities

PICCOLYTE S SERIES

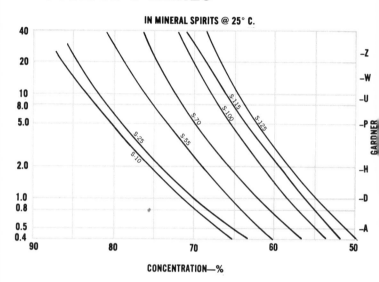

IN MINERAL SPIRITS @ 25° C.

CONCENTRATION—%

Solution Viscosities

PICCOLYTE ALPHA

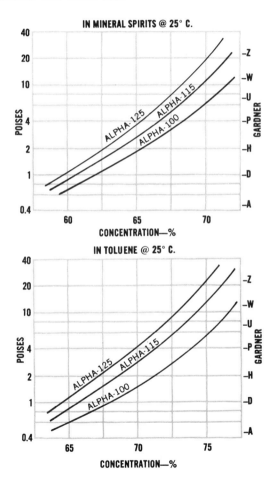

63

Solution Viscosities

RESINEX 100

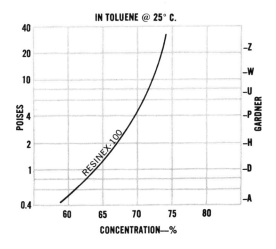

PICCOTEX

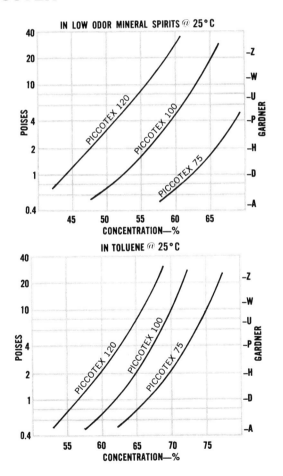

PICCOLASTIC

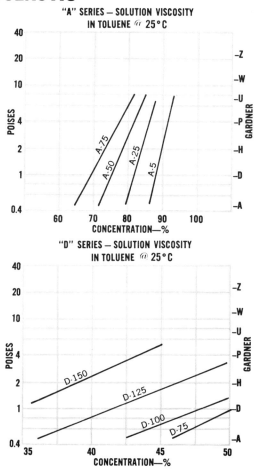

"A" SERIES — SOLUTION VISCOSITY
IN TOLUENE @ 25°C

"D" SERIES — SOLUTION VISCOSITY
IN TOLUENE @ 25°C

Solution Viscosities

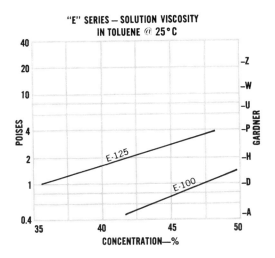

"E" SERIES — SOLUTION VISCOSITY
IN TOLUENE @ 25°C

HOT MELT VISCOSITIES

In the section "HOW RESINS DIFFER," "OBSERVATIONS NOT OTHERWISE CLASSIFIED," the hot melt viscosity of two resins is discussed and related to the flexibility of the polymer chain. The graph presented here is intended to suggest that resins be considered as "solid oils". Additional data on various softening points is available in individual product catalogues. For convenience, all the common grades of rubber processing resins have been plotted on one graph.

When dealing with the question of "hot tack", which is of interest to retreaders using directly extruded tread rubber, the results are affected by compatibility, surface effects, and molecular weight distribution. In addition, it is believed the viscosity of the resin, at the hot tack temperature, plays a part. While the variables have not been investigated sufficiently to allow exact predictions, this information is of use in the art of "intuitive" compounding.

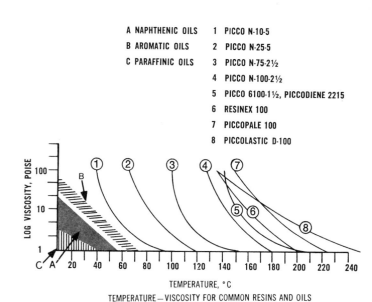

A NAPHTHENIC OILS	1 PICCO N-10-5
B AROMATIC OILS	2 PICCO N-25-5
C PARAFFINIC OILS	3 PICCO N-75-2½
	4 PICCO N-100-2½
	5 PICCO 6100-1½, PICCODIENE 2215
	6 RESINEX 100
	7 PICCOPALE 100
	8 PICCOLASTIC D-100

TEMPERATURE, °C

TEMPERATURE — VISCOSITY FOR COMMON RESINS AND OILS

SHELF LIFE OF RESIN SAMPLES

Unlike gold and platinum, resins are affected by the ravages of time and thus have a "shelf life." This list of recommended storage times is not intended as a clear cut index of when a resin will not perform. Instead, it is meant to be a guideline for those who are planning laboratory work and wonder whether they should request fresh samples.

Resinex, Flaked	6 months
Resinex, Solid	1 year
Picco N Resins, Flaked	6 months
Picco N Resins, Solid	1 year
Picco Resins, Flaked	6 months
Picco Resins, Solid	1 year
Piccopale SF Grades, Flaked	6 months
Piccopale SF Grades, Solid	1 year
Piccopale, Flaked	3 months
Piccopale, Solid	6 months
Piccolyte, Solid	6 months
Piccolastics, Flaked	1 year
Piccolastics, solid	2 years
Piccopale Emulsions	6 months
Piccotex, Solid	2 years
Piccoflex, Flaked	6 months
Piccoflex, Solid	1 year
Piccodiene, SRG Grades, Flaked	6 months
Piccodiene, SRG Grades, Solid	1 year

Hydrocarbon resins, particularly the terpenes, terpene phenolics, and petroleum-based resins, are primary modifiers for elastomers in all types of rubber-based adhesives.

Electrical insulation poses some critical problems in rubber compounding. Hydrocarbon resins not only assist in formulating the insulation material, but assure good adhesion to the conductor surface.

RESIN DESCRIPTIONS
AND PROPERTIES

Picco N Resins

Coumarone-Indene Resins were among the first products developed after the coal tar by-product industry undertook its initial expansion in the United States at the opening of World War I. Based on experimental work by Kraemer and Spilker who produced polymerized resin from certain coal tar light oil fractions in 1890, methods were soon developed for commercial production of the polymerized hydrocarbons known as Coumarone-Indene Resins.

Picco N Resins are neutral thermoplastic hydrocarbon polymers produced by the polymerization of olefins associated with the coal tar fraction distilling between 150° to 200° C. These resins have been referred to for many years as Coumarone-Indene Resins even though the coumarone content is very low. It has become accepted practice to graphically represent these resins as polyindene, although it is generally known they contain a number of aromatic olefins of the substituted styrene type, as well as some substituted indenes.

Picco N Series TYPICAL PROPERTIES

Name	Number	Color Coal Tar	Melting Point Ball & Ring	Specific Gravity	Bromine Elec. No.	Iodi No Cor rect
Picco	N-10-5	3-5	10°C	1.03	16	26
*Picco	N-25-5	3-5	35°C	1.05	16	26
Picco	N-75-2½	2-2½	75°C	1.07	14	22
Picco	N-100-½	½	100°C	1.09	12	19
Picco	N-100-1	1	100°C	1.09	12	19
Picco	N-100-1½	1½	100°C	1.09	12	19
Picco	N-100-2½	2-2½	100°C	1.09	12	19
**Picco	N-100-5	3-5	100°C	1.09	12	19
**Picco	N100-9	6-9	100°C	1.09	12	19
Picco	N-110-½	½	110°C	1.10	12	19
Picco	N-110-1	1	110°C	1.10	12	19
Picco	N-110-1½	1½	110°C	1.10	12	19
Picco	N-120-½	½	120°C	1.10	12	19
Picco	N-120-1	1	120°C	1.10	12	19
Picco	N-120-1½	1½	120°C	1.10	12	19

*Available in 25° C. softening point if desired by customer.

**Modified structure for applications where extra reinforcing properties are desired

MOONEY (ML/4/212) OF PICCO N-100-½ RESIN IN VARIOUS POLYMERS

phr Resin	Natural	SBR 1502	Neoprene W	BUTYL 218	HYCAR 1053
0	82	51	35	80	54
5	71	43	32	74	55
10	64	41	30	73	53
20	54	37	26	69	45
30	47	34	18	64	38

Picco Series

The PICCO Resin Series represents a family of petroleum derived polyindene or coumarone indene type resins. PICCO 100 resin is the best known member of the series. PICCO 100-3 resin,

72

Refract. Index	C.O.C. Flash Point	C.O.C. Fire Point	Acid Number Max.	Sapon. Number Max.	Melt Viscosity Degrees Centigrade		
					1 Ps.	10 Ps.	100 Ps.
1.58	350°F	390°F	<1	<1	95°	55°	40°
1.59	405°F	430°F	<1	<1	110°	85°	65°
1.62	435°F	485°F	<1	<1	150°	115°	100°
1.63	495°F	570°F	<1	<1	180°	150°	130°
1.63	495°F	570°F	<1	<1	180°	150°	130°
1.63	495°F	570°F	<1	<1	180°	150°	130°
1.63	495°F	570°F	<1	<1	180°	150°	130°
1.63	495°F	570°F	<1	<1	180°	150°	130°
1.63	495°F	570°F	<1	<1	180°	150°	130°
1.64	510°F	580°F	<1	<1	195°	165°	140°
1.64	510°F	580°F	<1	<1	195°	165°	140°
1.64	510°F	580°F	<1	<1	195°	165°	140°
1.64	550°F	590°F	<1	<1	205°	175°	150°
1.64	550°F	590°F	<1	<1	205°	175°	150°
1.64	550°F	590°F	<1	<1	205°	175°	150°

as it is known today, is rapidly being replaced by the lighter colored, lower cost, Picco 6100-1½ resin. A comparison of these resins with the Picco N (coal tar) series is to be found in the section on "What is Available."

At one time it was thought the coal tar resins were a little more compatible with neoprene and nitrile, hence the initial N as part of the coal tar resin nomenclature. This is no longer felt to be true and most major consumers of the so-called coumarone indene resins have changed to Picco 6100-1½ resin. Although the name "Picco Resin Series" is somewhat confusing because of the variety of Picco resins made, Picco 100-3 resin is still an important continuing product. The resin is used in a multitude of small applications that do not warrant the effort required to make the change.

Picco Series TYPICAL PROPERTIES

Name	Number	Color Coal Tar	Melting Point Ball & Ring	Specific Gravity	Bromine No. Elec.
Picco	AP-10-6	4-6	10°C	0.99	2.5
Picco	AP-25-5	3-5	30°C	1.00	3
Picco	100-2½	2-2½	100°C	1.05	17
Picco	100-3	3-5	100°C	1.05	17
Picco	110-2½	2-2½	110°C	1.05	17
Picco	110-5	3-5	110°C	1.05	17
Picco	110-9	6-9	110°C	1.05	17
Picco	120-2½	2-2½	120°C	1.05	17
Picco	120-5	3-5	120°C	1.05	17

MOONEY (ML/4/212) OF PICCO 100-3 RESIN IN VARIOUS POLYMERS

phr Resin	Natural	SBR 1502	Neoprene W	Butyl 218	Hycar 1053
0	82	51	35	80	54
5	72	47	32	72	48
10	68	46	28	70	45
20	44	38	21	64	44
30	44	34	16	61	44

Picco 6000 Series

PICCO 6100-1½, the most popular of the PICCO 6000 series of resins, was designed as an improvement in color and price as compared to the traditional coumarone indene resins. Although still very new, it has replaced both PICCO N-100-2½ (coal tar based) and PICCO 100-3 (petroleum based) resins in many applications. It performs well as a processing aid in nitrile and as a reinforcing resin in mineral filled neoprene and SBR.

The PICCO 6000 Series, like the old PICCO Series, is petroleum based. It reflects the recent availability of new streams of un-saturates available from the complex petrochemical industry. Except for an improved color there is very little difference between the PICCO 6000 Series and the time-honored PICCO 100 Series.

	Refract. Index	C.O.C. Flash Point	C.O.C. Fire Point	Acid Number Max.	Sapon. Number Max.	Melt Viscosity Degrees Centigrade		
						1 Ps.	10 Ps.	100 Ps.
	1.56	330°F	355°F	<1	<1	80°	50°	30°
	1.56	350°F	400°F	<1	<1	100°	70°	50°
	1.60	420°F	515°F	<1	<1	200°	160°	130°
	1.60	420°F	515°F	<1	<1	200°	160°	130°
	1.60	485°F	560°F	<1	<1	205°	165°	140°
	1.60	485°F	560°F	<1	<1	205°	165°	140°
	1.60	485°F	560°F	<1	<1	205°	165°	140°
	1.61	510°F	605°F	<1	<1	210°	175°	150°
	1.61	510°F	605°F	<1	<1	210°	175°	150°

Picco 6000 Series TYPICAL PROPERTIES

RESIN GRADE	6070-3	6100-1½	6115-1½	6120-3	6130-3	6140-3
Color, Coal Tar, max.	3	1½	1½	3	3	3
*Melting Point, deg. C	70	100	115	120	130	140
Specific Gravity	1.03	1.06	1.06	1.06	1.06	1.06
Bromine No. (elec.)	6.5	10.3	7.7	22	21	21
Iodine No. (corrected)	10.3	16.4	12.2	35	33	33
Refractive index, 25°C	1.57	1.60	1.59	1.56	1.56	1.57
COC Flash Point, °F	460	480	550	605	615	625
Acid number, max.	1.	1.	1.	1.	1.	1.
Saponification No., max.	1.	1.	1.	1.	1.	1.

*Ring and Ball Method

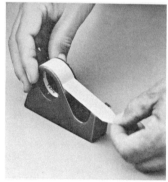

Versatility of hydrocarbon resins in rubber compounds is endless. They are in commercial use as tackifiers, plasticizers, extenders, wetting agents, and reinforcing agents in hundreds of different rubber applications.

Piccodiene Resins

The PICCODIENE resins are manufactured from selected streams of unsaturates from the petrochemical industry. The unsaturates include substantial amounts of dicyclopentadiene as well as the aromatic indene structures found in resins like PICCO 6100-1½. The net effect is to give a resin with a medium, or intermediate, aromatic content.

PICCODIENE 14215SRG resin is the most popular rubber grade although lighter colors and higher and lower softening points are available. Although the meaning of the initials "SRG" has been a source of humor, some obscene, they really stand for Stabilized, Rubber Grade. The 14 is the maximum coal tar color and the 215 the ball and ring softening point but in degrees F. in contrast to the usual method of nomenclature.

The other popular grade is PICCODIENE 2215SRG a resin with a maximum color of 2, using the coal tar scale.

TYPICAL PROPERTIES
Piccodiene 14215-SRG Rubber Resin

Color, coal tar scale	7
Melting point, ball and ring,	
°F	215
°C	100
Specific gravity	1.11
Pounds per gallon	9.25
Bromine number	55
Iodine number	180
Acid number, max.	<1
Saponification no., max.	<1

MOONEY (ML/4/212) OF PICCODIENE 2215SRG RESIN IN VARIOUS POLYMERS

phr Resin	Natural	SBR 1502	Neoprene W	Butyl 218	Hycar 1053
0	83	51	35	80	54
5	73	46	27	77	50
10	62	42	23	73	49
20	33	38	20	62	44
30	32	30	17	57	43

PROPERTIES OF PICCOPALE RESIN

The following are typical properties of all grades:

Color, Coal Tar Scale	2
Color, Gardner Scale	11
Color, Rosin Scale	E
Refractive Index	1.53
Specific Gravity	0.96 - 0.98
Pounds per gallon	8.01
Gallons per pound	0.1249
Pounds per gallon, 70% solution in mineral spirits	7.67
Specific Heat	0.45
Ash Content	less than 0.1%
Acid Number	less than 1
Saponification Number	less than 1
Dielectric constants:	100 cycles 2.33 $\pm$ 0.05
	10,000 cycles 2.33 $\pm$ 0.05
	1 megacycle 2.33 $\pm$ 0.05
	100 megacycles 2.33 $\pm$ 0.05
Loss Tangent:	100 cycles 0.0003
	10,000 cycles 0.0003
	1 megacycle 0.0005
	100 megacycles 0.0008 $\pm$ 0.0004

SPECIFIC GRADES	70,70SF*	85,85SF*	100, 100SF*	110, 110SF*
Melting Point, ball-and-ring *(ASTM)	70°C	85°C	100°C	100°C
Molecular Weight	800	1000	1400	1500
Bromine number (electrometric)	25	30	36	37
Iodine number (corrected)	40	50	60	60
Iodine number (Wijs method)	145	145	145	145
Flash point (C.O.C.)	450°F	475°F	510°F	550°F
Fire point (C.O.C.)	475°F	525°F	575°F	605°F

*Piccopale 70-SF, 85-SF, 100-SF, and 110-SF resins are stabilized to prevent absorption of oxygen.

Piccopale Resins

PICCOPALE is the trademark for a series of pale thermoplastic hydrocarbon resins derived from high temperature cracking of petroleum.

PICCOPALE resins are produced from chemical building-blocks of unsaturated hydrocarbons. Raw material for producing them is a mixture of monomers having an approximate average molecular weight of 90, and composed essentially of dienes and reactive olefins. These finished resins are unique because they are a mixture of straight-chain hydrocarbon resins in which considerable cyclic, but no aromatic, structures are present.

PICCOPALE resin was first developed to provide a low-cost thermoplastic polymer for the process industries. By utilizing petroleum as the source, an unlimited supply has been assured, as well as a stabilized cost foundation.

PICCOPALE resins are readily soluble in most aliphatic, aromatic, and chlorinated solvents. In addition, they have excellent compatibility with various forms of rosin (rosin esters, wood rosin and tall oil) as well as polyolefins such as polyethylene, polypropylene or waxes. These resins also are compatible with natural and synthetic rubber. (See page 10 for detailed information on compatibilities.)

In classification, they are not one of the "reactive" type such as the phenolic, urea-formaldehyde, or phenol-formaldehyde resins, which are thermo-setting. PICCOPALE resin belongs to the thermoplastic category.

The PICCOPALE resins should not be confused with other highly-oxidizable types of hydrocarbon resins.

MOONEY (ML/4/212) OF PICCOPALE 100SF RESIN IN VARIOUS POLYMERS

phr Resin	Natural	SBR 1502	Neoprene W	Butyl 218	Hycar 1053
0	82	51	35	80	54
5	71	45	31	74	48
10	62	42	27	68	43
20	37	38	20	54	37
30	35	33	20	46	30

Piccolyte S Resins   TYPICAL PROPERTIES

Name	Number	Color Gardner	Melting Point Ball & Ring	Specific Gravity	Bromi No. Elec
Piccolyte	S-10	4	10°C	0.94	5
Piccolyte	S-25	4	25°C	0.95	5
Piccolyte	S-40	4	40°C	0.95	5
Piccolyte	S-55	4	55°C	0.96	5
Picoclyte	S-70	4	70°C	0.97	5
Piccolyte	S-85	4	85°C	0.97	5
Piccolyte	S-100	4	100°C	0.97	5
Piccolyte	S-115	4	115°C	0.97	5
Piccolyte	S-125	4	125°C	0.98	5
Piccolyte	S-135	4	135°C	0.98	5

Piccolyte Alpha Resins

PICCOLYTE Alpha resin is made from alpha pinene, one of the principal constituents of turpentine. Unlike the traditional naval stores resins it is a pure hydrocarbon and not an organic acid. Because of this, the PICCOLYTE Alpha resins are very hydrophobic and have but very little tendency for chemical reaction.

Piccolyte Alpha Resins

Softening Point, °C.
Color, Gardner
Acid Number, (less than)
Saponification Number, (less than)
Bromine Number, (Elec.)
Iodine Number, (calculated)
Specific Gravity
Refractive Index
Ash Content, Max. %
Flash Point, °F.
Fire Point, °F.
Melt Viscosity, °C.
   1 poise
   10 poises
   100 poises
Chlorine content
   (Bielstein test)

The PICCOLYTE resins are terpene derivative, the S grades being made from beta Pinene and the Alpha grades from alpha Pinene. They are characterized by very light color and good stability. They are widely used in adhesives and tapes.

Iodine No. Corrected	Refract. Index	C.O.C. Flash Point	C.O.C. Fire Point	Acid Number Max.	Sapon. Number Max.	Melt Viscosity Degrees Centigrade		
						1 Ps.	10 Ps.	100 Ps.
8	1.51	425°F	475°F	<1	<1	110°	75°	50°
8	1.51	425°F	475°F	<1	<1	125°	80°	60°
8	1.52	425°F	475°F	<1	<1	135°	100°	75°
8	1.52	425°F	475°F	<1	<1	150°	115°	90°
8	1.53	425°F	475°F	<1	<1	170°	130°	100°
8	1.53	425°F	475°F	<1	<1	190°	145°	115°
8	1.53	425°F	475°F	<1	<1	200°	155°	130°
8	1.53	500°F	550°F	<1	<1	210°	175°	145°
8	1.52	500°F	550°F	<1	<1	215°	180°	155°
8	1.52	500°F	550°F	<1	<1	235°	195°	165°

PICCOLYTE Alpha resin is a new polymer developed to meet the increased demands of the adhesive industries for terpene resins. Due to the limited supply of beta pinene, the future needs of the adhesives field for exceptional tackifiers can not be met entirely by the old standby, the PICCOLYTE S series of resins.

For the same softening point the Alpha resins have a lower hot melt viscosity and a lower molecular weight than the beta

TYPICAL PROPERTIES

Alpha 10	Alpha 25	Alpha 40	Alpha 55	Alpha 70	Alpha 85	Alpha 100	Alpha 115	Alpha 125	Alpha 135
10	25	40	55	70	85	100	115	125	135
4	4	4	4	4	4	4	4	4	4
1	1	1	1	1	1	1	1	1	1
1	1	1	1	1	1	1	1	1	1
30	30	30	30	30	30	30	30	30	30
48	48	48	48	48	48	48	48	48	48
0.93	0.94	0.94	0.95	0.96	0.96	0.97	0.97	0.97	0.97
1.51	1.51	1.52	1.52	1.52	1.52	1.53	1.53	1.53	1.53
0.1	0.1	0.1	0.1	0.1	0.1	0.1	0.1	0.1	0.1
415	415	420	425	425	425	425	425	450	460
450	450	455	460	460	460	460	460	500	510
100	110	125	150	160	170	185	200	210	225
60	80	90	105	120	133	155	165	175	195
40	55	70	85	100	110	128	145	155	170
Neg.	Neg.	Neg.	Neg.	Neg.	Neg.	Neg.	Neg.	Neg.	Neg.

pinene resins. With some modifications, to compensate for the lower molecular weight, natural rubber pressure sensitive adhesives can be formulated which are equivalent to those made from the PICCOLYTE S grades. In addition, good adhesives can be compounded using SBR as the base polymer, this being in contrast to the beta resins.

Piccolastic Resins

PICCOLASTIC resins are pure polystyrene, but with molecular weights much lower than the molding grades. They are unique in physical properties, because they combine the toughness and other desirable properties of polystyrene, but they have the ease of handling usually attributed to ester gums and petroleum resins. They are many times more versatile in compounding than molding grade polystyrene.

THE "A" SERIES

This series includes the softest and most compatible form of PICCOLASTIC resin. The lower-molecular-weight resins of this series are actually liquid polymers at room temperature. These are excellent softeners and primary plasticizers, and where they show compatibility, are non-migrating. Their fluidity promotes easier processing when they are incorporated into commercial compounds.

The "A" series resins are compatible in all proportions with aliphatic solvents and with paraffin waxes. A-5, A-25, and A-50 are also compatible with high-melting point microcrystalline waxes. Properties of A-75, hardest in this series, are influenced by its higher molecular weight and melting point, and is somewhat less soluble and show slightly less compatibility. All resins in this series, including the liquid resins, are all pure polymers, containing no monomer or solvent.

PICCOLASTIC T-135 RESIN

This is a special grade of solid PICCOLASTIC resin which has a relatively high molecular weight, but has both lower cost and darker color than other grades. It is used where high viscosity and dark colors may be tolerated.

THE "D" SERIES

This series is an intermediate range in molecular weights, but considerably harder and tougher than the "A" series. While hard

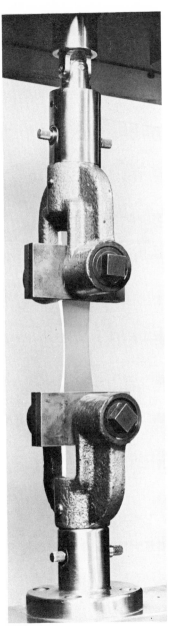

Among hydrocarbon resins,
PICCOLASTIC series are
outstanding in
tensile properties.

and tough—the characteristic properties of PICCOLASTIC resins—this series is still readily workable, retains some wetting qualities, and is probably the most versatile in the PICCOLASTIC family of resins.

As binder resins, all in the "D" series are excellent. Their tensile strength, combined with resiliency, produces products and coatings which are durable and shock resistant. The "D" series is hard and very dry, with not a trace of tackiness until the resin is melted.

To plasticize the "D" series, a resin from the PICCOLASTIC "A" family may be used. The close similarity of the two groups provides a completely homogenious compound—a true solution, with no possible migration. Otherwise, the usual alkyl-aryl plasticizers may be employed. The "D" series is compatible to a limited degree with white mineral oil and paraffin wax, but not at all with microcrystalline waxes. A solvent with a minimum

Piccolastic Resins TYPICAL PROPERTIES

Name	Number	Color Gardner	Melting Point Ball & Ring	Specific Gravity	Bromine No. Elec.	Iodine No. Corrected	Refrac Inde
Piccolastic	A-5	5	5°C	1.02	4	6.5	1.57
Piccolastic	A-25	5	25°C	1.03	3	5	1.58
Piccolastic	A-50	5	50°C	1.04	2	3	1.58
Piccolastic	A-75	3	75°C	1.05	1	1.6	1.60
Piccolastic	D-75	5	75°C	1.05	1	1.6	1.58
Piccolastic	D-100	5	100°C	1.07	1	1.6	1.59
Piccolastic	D-125	5	125°C	1.06	1	1.6	1.60
Piccolastic	D-150	5	145°C	1.06	1	1.6	1.60
Piccolastic	E-50	5	50°C	1.05	2	3	1.58
Piccolastic	E-75	5	75°C	1.05	1.5	2.5	1.58
Piccolastic	E-100	5	100°C	1.06	1.0	1.6	1.58
Piccolastic	E-125	5	125°C	1.06	1.0	1.6	1.60
Piccolastic	T-135	10	135°C	1.06	5	8	1.59

Kauributanol (KB) rating of 45 is required for completely dissolving the D-75 and D-100 grades, a KB of 60 minimum for D-125 and 100% xylol is required for D-150.

THE "E" SERIES

The "E" (or elastic) series have been specifically developed to promote the greatest elasticity possible in polystyrene. This series ranges in melting points from 50° C. to 125° C. They have a set of physical characteristics which set them apart from the rest of this family of resins, in that they lack the wetting power, in some cases, but replace this with a unique type of adhesion which is discussed below.

The series possesses somewhat better solvent-power and compatibility than the "D" series, but not as much as the "A" series. Solvent power and compatibility decrease with melting point increase.

C.O.C. Flash Point	C.O.C. Fire Point	Acid Number Max.	Sapon. Number Max.	Melt Viscosity Degrees Centigrade			Estimated Molecular Weight
				1 Ps.	10 Ps.	100 Ps.	
370°F	420°F	<1	<1	70°	45°	30°	300
405°F	455°F	<1	<1	80°	60°	40°	325
445°F	520°F	<1	<1	120°	90°	70°	350
535°F	590°F	<1	<1	150°	115°	95°	400
460°F	515°F	<1	<1	240°	175°	125°	800
505°F	575°F	<1	<1	250°	180°	135°	1500
565°F	610°F	<1	<1		260°	195°	3000
600°F	645°F	<1	<1			250°	5000
445°F	480°F	<1	<1	180°	115°		1000
470°F	525°F	<1	<1	260°	180°	125°	2000
535°F	580°F	<1	<1		210°	150°	3500
555°F	590°F	<1	<1			200°	
590°F	640°F	<1	<1			230°	6000

Piccotex Resins

PICCOTEX resin is an unusually clear, glass-like synthetic polymer which is especially useful in compounding light-colored products. It exhibits excellent resistance to discoloration or yellowing caused by oxidation, heat, or ultraviolet exposure. It is also resistant to moisture, salt water, acids and alkalis.

PICCOTEX resin is a vinyl toluene, alpha methyl styrene copolymer, and is completely saturated. It has an aromatic ring structure, but it is soluble in low cost aliphatic solvents . . . such as Stoddard solvent or low odor mineral spirits . . . as well as aromatic and chlorinated solvents. PICCOTEX resin has excellent solution stability even at 1% and 2% solids in prolonged exposure to sunlight.

TYPICAL PROPERTIES

	Piccotex 75	Piccotex 100	Piccotex 120
Softening point, ball-and-ring	75°C	100°C	120°C.
Color, Gardner scale (maximum)	1	1	1
Specific gravity	1.04	1.04	1.04
Pounds per gallon, solid resin	8.67	8.67	8.67
Gardner viscosity, in toluene at 25° C	—	Q at 70% solids	L at 65% solids
Gardner viscosity, in 55% mineral spirits	—	—	T-V
Acid number, less than	1	1	1
Saponification number, less than	1	1	1
Bromine number (electrometric), less than	1	1	1
Ash, less than	0.1%	0.1%	0.1%
Refractive index at 25°C	1.583	1.583	1.583
Ozone number	0	0	0
Flash point, °F	470	505	540
Fire point, °F	535	570	585

Resinex Resins

RESINEX resins are a series of dark (Coal Tar Color 23), staining, low cost resinous materials recovered in a process for the manufacture of unsaturated aromatic resin forming fractions.

In this process, selected petroleum oils are cracked under carefully controlled conditions of temperature and pressure in order to obtain unsaturated aromatics. In this way, petroleum is made to yield products similar to those previously obtained only from the coking of coal.

RESINEX resin is a mixture of low molecular weight polymers of polycyclic unsaturated monomers having high carbon to hydrogen ratios, substantial amounts of the polymerized unsaturates being in the coumarone-indene range. These resins contain less than 0.5% free carbon. Being entirely hydrocarbon, they are highly resistant to moisture, acids and alkalies. The higher melting resins have a dense polycyclic molecular structure; they are not very soluble in aliphatic solvents. Although entirely hydrocarbon, these resins are not readily flammable. They will burn but they do not support combustion.

RESINEX L-4, 100 and 115 resins are the popular grades but intermediate softening points are available.

TYPICAL PROPERTIES

	Resinex 100	Resinex L-4
Softening Point	100°C	Liquid
Saybolt Viscosity at 210°F	—	45-55 SSU
Color, Coal Tar Scale	22	22
Specific Gravity	1.14	1.06
Acid Number	<1	<1
Saponification Number	<1	<1
Flash Point, C.O.C.	500°F	300°F
Fire Point, C.O.C.	550°F	330°F
Ash	<0.1%	<0.1%
Benzene Insoluble	Nil	Nil
Melt Viscosity		
210°C	1 poise	—
165°C	10 poises	—
138°C	100 poise	—
25°C		3 poises
Solution Viscosity in Toluene		
% Solids		
50	0.3 poises	—
60	0.5 poises	—
70	5.2 poises	—

MOONEY (ML/4/212) OF RESINEX 100 RESIN IN VARIOUS POLYMERS

phr Resin	Natural	SBR 1502	Neoprene W	Butyl 218	Hycar 1053
0	82	51	35	80	54
5	80	47	31	76	51
10	77	43	26	75	48
20	70	34	23	68	41
30	65	38	19	65	37

Piccopale Resin Emulsions

PICCOPALE emulsions are stable dispersions of an unsaponifiable hydrocarbon resin in water. Upon removal of the water and an essential part of the emulsifier system by evaporation, absorption, or neutralization, the resin particles resume their hydrophobic character and form a moisture and water-resistant coating.

In the nine PICCOPALE emulsions available, films produced range from soft and tacky at room temperatures to coatings of discrete resin particles which require heat to coalesce.

Where tougher or more flexible continuous films are required, emulsions of film forming polymers may be combined with the PICCOPALE Emulsions.

PICCOPALE resin emulsions are available in three major categories: Anionic, Cationic and Non-ionic.

TYPICAL PROPERTIES

EMULSION	A-1	A-3	A-20	A-22	A-41	A-43	A-55	C-1	N-3
Type Emulsifier	A	A	A	A	A	A	A	C	N
pH	8.8	8.8	10.3	4.5	10.5	10.5	10.5	6.0	8.8
Total Solids, %	50	50	50	50	45	45	50	50	50
Maximum Particle Size, Microns	1	1	1	1	1	1	1	1	1
Viscosity, cps @ 20° C.*	1400	1400	70	60	40	30	35	300	100
Surface Tension, dynes/centimeter	32	32	33	29	35	36	38	37	32
Specific Gravity	0.97	0.97	0.97	0.98	1.00	1.00	0.99	0.99	0.98
Emulsion, lbs/gal	8.12	8.12	8.12	8.18	8.35	8.35	8.24	8.24	8.19
Storage Stability	E	E	E	E	E	E	E	G	G
Mechanical Stability	F	F	G	E	E	E	E	E	G
Dried Film	S	S	H	H	H	H	H†	H‡	

*Brookfield No. 1 Spindle @ 20 RPM.   E = Excellent   G = Good   F = Fair
A — Anionic   C — Cationic   N — Non-ionic
Dried Film: S = Soft   H = Hard   H† = Harder   H‡ = No film, requires heat to coalesce.

TEST METHODS

Viscosity	ASTM D-1417 - 57 - T
Storage Stability	Periodic Inspection
Surface Tension	ASTM D-1417 - 57 - T
Total Solids	Garvimetric in convection oven
Mechanical Stability	ASTM D-1076 - 59
Particle Size	Optical Method, Calibrated eyepiece

Coumarone Indene Resin Emulsion

Typical Analysis

Type Resin	Polyindene
Type Emusifier	Anionic
pH	11.0
Total Solids	50%
Viscosity, cps (Brookfield)	30
Surface Tension, dynes/centimeter	36
Mechanical Stability	Excellent
Color	Light Cream
Specific Gravity	1.055
Pounds per Gallon	8.79
Particular Size	< 1 Micron
Dilutibility With Water	Infinite

Semi-Aromatic Resin Emulsion

PICCO A-15 EMULSION

PICCO A-15 is an anionic emulsion of a semi aromatic hydrocarbon resin. It is useful as a modifier for latex and polymer emulsion systems. PICCO A-15 EMULSION provides a means of improving and controlling tack in rubber latex systems, and is particularly valuable as a component in latex adhesives.

The low cost of PICCO A-15 EMULSION provides a means of developing optimum physical characteristics in natural and synthetic rubber compounds at economical levels.

This emulsion provides improved wetting of pigments and fillers, which leads to higher loading and, consequently, higher profits in finished goods.

TYPICAL PROPERTIES

Type Resin	Semi-Aromatic
Type Emulsifier	Anionic
Resin Color, coal tar scale	5
ph	11.5
Total Solids	50%
Particle Size, maximum	1 micron
Viscosity, Brookfield*	70 cps
Surface Tension	39 dynes/cm
Mechanical Stability**	Excellent
Storage Stability	Excellent
Weight per gallon of emulsion	8.42 pounds
Ion Tolerances:	
Sulfuric Acid	Poor
Hydrochloric Acid	Poor
Acetic Acid	Poor
Potassium Chloride	Excellent
Sodium Chloride	Good
Calcium Chloride	Poor
Aluminum Sulfate	Poor
Sodium Hydroxide	Fair
Potassium Hydroxide	Excellent
Ammonium Hydroxide	Excellent

* Model RVF, Spindle No. 1 at 20 RPM
** Modified Hamilton Beach

Terpene Resin Emulsions

TYPICAL PROPERTIES

	PICCOLYTE S-70 EMULSION	PICCOLYTE 2788 EMULSION
Type Resin	Poly Beta Pinene	Poly Alpha Pinene
Type Emulsifier	Anionic	Anionic
pH	8.0	11.0
Total Solids	50%	55%
Brookfield Viscosity	2000 cps	500 cps
Surface Tension	32 dynes/cm	38 dynes/cm
Emulsion Color	Very Light Cream	Light Cream
Specific Gravity	0.975	0.990
Pounds per Gallon	8.12	8.25
Particle Size	<1 Micron	<1 Micron
Mechanical Stability	Fair	Fair Excellent
Storage Stability	Excellent	Good

Other Picco Resin Emulsions

Type Resin...EVA* modified petroleum resin

TYPICAL PROPERTIES

	PICCO A-60 EMULSION	PICCO A-62 EMULSION Acid Stable Emulsifier
ph	11.0	11.0
Total Solids	55%	55%
Brookfield Viscosity	200 cps	300 cps
Surface Tension	36 dynes/cm	36 dynes/cm
Emulsion Color	Light Cream	Light Cream
Specific Gravity	1.025	1.025
Pounds per Gallon	8.6	8.6
Particle Size	<1 Micron	<1 Micron
Mechanical Stability	Excellent	Excellent
Storage Stability	Excellent	Excellent

*Ethylene—vinyl acetate copolymer

Picco Phenolic Resins

The traditional PICCO resins are completely hydrocarbon in nature, being devoid of functional chemical groups. The PICCO Phenolic Resins are different. Although they look like other PICCO hydrocarbon resins and are non-reactive, thermoplastic resins, they differ in compatibility, solubility and tackifying action. They vary in respect to the hydroxyl group concentration introduced through the phenol and in the degree of hindering or masking the chemical reactivity of this functional group.

They also differ with regard to the kind and amount of alkylating group used to raise molecular weight and control solubility. With one exception, the alkylating group is a terpene, hence, the name Phenolic Resins. They should not be confused with other resins containing rosin or rosin derivatives.

LTP-100, LTP-115, LTP-135 Resins: Available in three softening points and used as tackifying resins for SBR, natural rubber and neoprene, particularly to increase the open time of cements. While the OH groups give a much broader compatability and solubility than a conventional terpene resin, their potential chemical reactivity is effectively masked. They exhibit unusually good color stability. They lend strong antioxidant properties and are being investigated for synergistic effects in combination with traditional antioxidants and UV light absorbers. Helpful as a very low viscosity modifying resin for lacquers and hot melt polyamide formulations.

ETP-105 Resin: Just the opposite of the LTP resins in that the OH groups are predominant. This gives alcohol solubility. Useful as a modifier for epoxy esters and two-compartment epoxy systems. Of interest for PVAc adhesives, grease-repellent lacquers, and gasoline repellent coatings. Also may be useful in alkaline water systems.

NTP-90 Resin: The solubility and OH reactivity are balanced to make this resin a good rubber tackifier for tire carcass stocks, belts, hose and innerliners. Also useful in cooked hard oil varnish.

NRP-90 Resin: This is not a terpene phenolic resin. NRP-90 is a non-reactive, alkyl phenolic resin. In composition and function it is much like the NTP-90 resin but the change in alkylating agent gives a further refinement in solubility characteristics.

TYPICAL PHYSICAL PROPERTIES

Resin	LTP-100	LTP-115	LTP-135	ETP-105	NTP-90	NRP-90
Color (Gardner)	7	7	7	7	7	8
Softening Point (Ball & Ring)	100°C.	115°C.	135°C.	150°C	90°C.	90°C.
Acid No.	Nil	Nil	Nil	3	5	28
Specific Gravity	1.02	1.02	1.03	1.03	1.05	1.04
Methylol Content	None	None	None	None	Trace	Trace

A WORD ABOUT PICCO

If you've ever changed a tire, used cellophane tape, chewed a stick of gum, walked on a tile floor, or, with dripping arm, painted a ceiling, the chance is good that you've come in contact with a PICCO product. Pennsylvania Industrial Chemical Corporation—known to the industrial world as "PICCO"—has been the major manufacturer of synthetic hydrocarbon resins for more than forty years.

Robert W. Ostermayer, Sr. directed PICCO's entry into the resin business, in the mid-twenties. He is still very active as chairman of the corporation's board of directors. Through application of his philosophies over the years, PICCO has become one of the most respected names in the chemical industry. PICCO's first products were resins and solvents made from coke by-products; diversification into products made from petroleum followed in the late thirties, and products made from by-products of the wood and paper industry were developed in the early forties. Today, in addition to these older products, polymers are tailor-made from pure chemical materials.

PICCO operates three plants in Pennsylvania—at Chester, a suburb of Philadelphia; at Clairton, just outside Pittsburgh; and at West Elizabeth, near Clairton. There are also PICCO plants in Baton Rouge, Louisiana, and in Tuscaloosa, Alabama. Each plant is self-contained and is completely staffed for maintenance, quality control and production. Research, development and engineering functions are centered at the home office in Clairton. Processes used at these plants include polymerization, alkylation, distillation, filtration, extrusion, as well as the normal plant service and utility units.

Starting as a small-volume producer of a limited variety of products, PICCO is now the world's foremost producer of low molecular weight hydrocarbon resins. These resins find use in not only tire, tape, gum, floor tile and paint applications, of course, but also in virtually every corner of industrial and consumer use throughout the world. And the list of applications is growing every day. In all these developments, PICCO has been a leader, not a follower.

BIBLIOGRAPHY

[1] E. I. duPont de Nemours & Co. (Inc.) Rubber Chemicals Division, Report BL-121, Sept. 18, 1943.

[2] J. T. Blake, "Synthetic Rubber", J. Wiley & Sons, Inc., New York, 1954,

[3] PICCO Bulletin PPN-069, PICCO 6000 Series Used in Rubber

[4] T. A. Bulifant, Rubber Age, 62, #300-2 (1947).

[5] C. E. Morrell, "Synthetic Rubber," J. Wiley & Sons, Inc., New York, 1954, G. S. Whitby, Editor-in-Chief, p. 62.

[6] PICCO Bulletin PPN-100, PICCOPALE Resins.

PICCO Bulletin PPN-101, PICCOMARON—PICCOVAR Resins.

PICCO Bulletin PPN-068, PICCO 6000 Series Resins.

PICCO Bulletin PPN-078, PICCO Terpene Phenolic Resins.

PICCO Bulletin PPN-089, PICCODIENE Resins.

PICCO Bulletin PPN-047, PICCODIENE SRG—for the Rubber Industry.

PICCO Bulletin PPN-049, PICCO Resins for the Rubber Industry.

PICCO Bulletin PPN-069, PICCO 6000 Series Resins for the Rubber Industry.

PICCO Bulletin PPN-091, PICODIENE 14215-SRG Resin for Rubber.

[7] PICCO Bulletin PPN-019, PICCOPALE Emulsion Catalog.

PICCO Bulletin PPN-105, PICCOPALE Emulsion A-55 in Latex Systems.

PICCO Bulletin PPN-023, PICCOPALE A-1 Emulsion Paints.

[8] P. J. Corish, Rubber Chem. Technol. 40, 324, (1967).

[9] F. S. Billmeyer, "Textbook of Polymer Chemistry", Interscience Publishers, Inc., New York, 1957.

[10] L. E. Nielsen, "Mechanical Properties of Polymers", Reinhold Publishing Corp., New York, 1962, p. 13.

[11] J. D. Skewis, Rubber Chem. Technol. 38, 689 (1965).

[12] J. D. Skewis, Rubber Chem. Technol. 39, 217 (1966).

[13] F. C. Weissert and B. L. Johnson, Rubber Chem. Technol. 40, 590, (1967).

[14] H. K. deDecker and D. J. Sabatine, Rubber Age, 99, 73, (1967).

[15] K. A. Grosch, L. Mullins, Rev. Gen. Caoutchouc, 39, 1781-1792, (1962).

[16] O. W. Burke, Jr., "Reinforcement of Elastomers", Interscience Publishers, New York, 1965, G. Kraus, Editor, pp. 510-511.

[17] A. K. Doolittle, "The Technology of Solvents and Plasticizers", J. Wiley, New York, 1954, pp. 870-871.

[18] O. W. Burke, Jr., "Reinforcement of Elastomers", Interscience Publishers, New York, 1965, G. Kraus, Editor, p. 491.

[19] D. Parkinson, Reinforcement of Rubbers, The Institution of the Rubber Industry, 1957, p. 1.

[20] C. W. Hock and A. N. Abbott, Rubber Age, 82, 471, (1957).

[21] D. J. Cram and G. S. Hammond, "Organic Chemistry", McGraw-Hill, New York, 1959, p. 149.

[22] H. Burrell, Offic. Dig. Feder. Soc. Paint Technol. 27, 726-758 (1955).

[23] PICCO Bulletin PPN-092, Solubility Contours for Picco Resins.

[24] Shell Chemical Co., Preliminary Data Sheet, Kraton 101, SCR 65-159.

[25] P. O. Powers, Rubber Chem. Technol. 36, 1551 (1963).

[26] O. K. F. Bussemaker, Rubber Chem. Technol. 37, 1178 (1964).

[27] A. V. Tobolsky, "Properties and Structures of Polymers", J. Wiley & Sons, New York, 1960, 1. 81.

ACKNOWLEDGEMENTS

I would like to recognize that James Kelly of Picco first pointed out to me the unique characteristics of resins in terms of their glass transition temperatures.

Fred Weissert of Firestone Research made a further contribution by relating this to properties of the vulcanizate.

Vernon Folt of Goodrich Research caused me to rethink the meaning of processing and compatibility.

Harvey Greer of Harwick reminded me to remember the "working stiff" as I labored at the typewriter.

Many others from Harwick, Picco and the rubber companies were kind enough to read the text and offer corrections and suggestions. To all of these go my thanks.

Gardner Brown

P.S. and to Ruth Brown, one of Miss Griffith's better students, for correcting an engineer's syntax.

INDEX